THE BOOK OF BRITAIN'S MIGHTIEST PASSENGER LOCOMOTIVE

FOR BOYS OF ALL AGES

The "King" of Railway Locomotives

THE BOOK OF BRITAIN'S MIGHTIEST PASSENGER LOCOMOTIVE

For Boys of all Ages

By

W. G. CHAPMAN

(*Author of "The 10.30 Limited," "Caerphilly Castle," and "'Twixt Rail and Sea"*)

PUBLISHED IN 1928 BY

THE GREAT WESTERN RAILWAY

[FELIX J. C. POLE, GENERAL MANAGER,]

PADDINGTON STATION, LONDON

First published 1928
Reprinted 1971

ISBN 0 85059 068 X

Reproduced by offset lithography from the original by Reda SA, of Geneva, Switzerland, and bound by Hunter & Foulis Ltd, of Edinburgh, Scotland, for the publishers Patrick Stephens Limited, 9 Ely Place, London EC1N 6SQ, England.

INTRODUCTION TO NEW EDITION

AFTER "Caerphilly Castle", which was first published in 1924 following the introduction of the Castle Class, it was logical that the G.W.R. would want to publish a book about the Kings. The first of the class, No. 6000 *King George V* was completed in June 1927, and no time was lost in publicising the event. On August 3rd, "*K.G.V.*" was shipped from Cardiff docks on the SS *Chicago City* bound for Baltimore, U.S.A., to lead the procession of big engines at "The Fair of the Iron Horse". One of the most moving chapters of this book fully describes the whole episode.

In addition we have a full account of "Kings in the Making" and the familiar story of G.W.R. locomotive evolution. Finally, the customary conversation on the train takes place on "The 10.30 Limited" but this time on the footplate and not in the compartment. The description of the scene on No. 1 Platform before departure is fascinating. The platform is thronged with happy holiday makers and "you notice that there is an atmosphere of joyful anticipation amongst them".

"You see these travellers are *not* worried by pot-holes, the perfume of petrol or the dangerous proximity of racing motor coaches. Nervous tension and the risks of congested highways are alike absent and they can read in comfort, enjoy a meal, and a quiet nap". All this in 1928! Except for the curiously dated style, the choice of phrase and the reference to pot-holes, it could all be true today.

The book is extremely well illustrated, and particularly noteworthy are the photographs recording the making of the "Kings" and events during the U.S.A. tour.

Norman Simmons

FOREWORD

"SOMEWHERE in the breast of every normal *homo sapiens* there stretches a chord which vibrates only to the sight of a fine locomotive. Even now, with airplanes and motors to bid against it in its own field of romantic interest, the steam locomotive retains its fascination."

That quotation, from the *New York Herald Tribune* of July 21, 1927, was inspired by the news that the Great Western Railway of England was sending to the Baltimore and Ohio Railroad Centenary Exhibition the locomotive "King George V," the first of the new "King" class of passenger engines.

Four years before this "Caerphilly Castle," the prototype of the "Castle" class, had made her debut as the most powerful passenger locomotive in the Kingdom. It says something for railway progress that within so short a space of time the same railway—always renowned for the power and speed of its engines—should produce the "King" class of locomotives with a tractive effort no less than 27·4 per cent in excess of the "Castles."

The coming of the "Kings" marks an epoch in the history of locomotive engineering, and the interest and admiration which these engines have evoked in both hemispheres is sufficient justification for the appearance of "The 'King' of Railway Locomotives—the Book of Britain's Mightiest Passenger Locomotive for Boys of All

FOREWORD

Ages," the fourth volume of the Great Western Railway " Boys of All Ages " series.

It is dedicated to that ever-growing army of young railway lovers who have evinced so much interest in the previous volumes in the series—" The 10.30 Limited," " Caerphilly Castle," and " 'Twixt Rail and Sea "—with the hope that the fourth and youngest member of the family may prove as popular as its three brothers.

W. G. C.

READING, *July*, 1928

CHAPTERS

WITH 110 ILLUSTRATIONS

CHAPTER THE FIRST

INTRODUCING THE "KINGS"

GOOD morning. I think I can divine the purpose of this visit. You come on the business of "Kings.". . . Exactly.

You want to know about as much as there is to know of the new wonder locomotives of the Great Western Railway. Well, we must see what can be done to assuage this commendable thirst for knowledge.

When discussing the stately "Castles" a few short years ago, we little dreamt that their great power would so soon be excelled. But we are privileged to live in an age of mechanical wonders, where one engineering marvel follows hot-foot on the heels of another. Railway locomotives are no exception in this respect, and just as you are bigger and stronger than when "Caerphilly Castle" was our subject, so locomotives of the "King" class of to-day are greater and more powerful than the "Castles" of yesterday. You are not the first young railway enthusiast who has deposed other favourites for the mighty "Kings"

—in fact (to parody), it seems to be a case of " Naught is the ' *Castle* ' when the ' King ' is nigh."

" But," you say, " why build these super-locomotives when the ' Castles ' and others are so speedy and powerful ? " I think the answer to that question is to be found in the progressive policy of the Great Western Railway—a railway which has ever been in the forefront of locomotive construction ; in the continuous growth of train loads ; and in the desire of the Company still further to improve the average speeds of its crack trains.

For about a quarter of a century the Great Western Railway has been steadily making its main lines suitable for more powerful locomotives in anticipation of traffic requirements warranting their introduction, and a good deal of foresight has been displayed in the way in which bridges have been strengthened and permanent way generally improved in order to prepare for bigger, and still bigger, locomotives.

Then I surmise that there may also be another explanation. You will remember that in April 1924 Their Majesties the King and Queen visited the Swindon Works where G.W.R. locomotives are built and that, at the conclusion of the royal tour, King George not only evinced a keen interest in engine No. 4082 " Windsor Castle," attached to the royal train, but also, with the Queen on the footplate beside him, drove it from the Works over the three-quarters of a mile to Swindon station. Now it *may* be that the Chief Mechanical Engineer, proud as he was of His Majesty's interest in and admiration for the " Castles," there and then made some sort of a vow to eclipse his previous efforts and produce a yet mightier engine, which

INTRODUCING THE "KINGS"

"King George V"—The first of the G.W.R. "King" Class of Passenger Locomotives; the most powerful in the Kingdom.

should be even more worthy of royal favour. I wonder if that was so? Anyway, the theory seems to be strengthened (don't you think ?) by the naming of the first of the new engines " King George V."

The creation of this new type of passenger express locomotive deservedly aroused widespread interest. Competition in achievement is highly desirable, as being productive of the best, and not only Great Western Railway employees but a wide circle of well-wishers and enthusiasts had anxiously inquired whether the Great Western Railway Company would surrender the honour of possessing the most powerful express passenger locomotive in the country. The production of the " Kings " is the answer to the question.

Before being actually put into traffic the first of the "Kings" was on view at some of the principal stations of the Great Western Railway, where it was critically inspected and duly approved by thousands of railway enthusiasts " of all ages." Here we see schoolboy locomotive experts literally swarming over the engine at Plymouth.

" King George V's " service career commenced on July 20, 1927, by taking the Cornish Riviera Express (" The 10.30 Limited ") from Paddington to Plymouth. Nothing so much impressed those who travelled on the train on this occasion as the extraordinary ease with which the task was accomplished. Records were neither attempted nor expected with a new locomotive so recently out of the shops, but the performance more than satisfied all concerned that the new engine could handle with ease and at high speed the heavy loads for which she had been designed. Although some time was lost due to service

[*Topical*

A critical inspection of "King George V" by schoolboys at Plymouth.

slacks, etc., the 155¼ miles from Slough to Exeter was actually covered at an average speed of 61·3 m.p.h. and the train arrived at destination five minutes under schedule.

The outstanding feature of the run was the unpiloted ascent of the Dainton and Rattery banks. The train weighed 410 tons behind the tender (excluding passengers and luggage) as far as Westbury, where two coaches were slipped, and 338 tons beyond; being then the heaviest passenger train load ever worked over the Dainton and Rattery banks by one engine.

You will get a better appreciation of the power of these mighty "Kings" when I tell you that the maximum loads of passenger trains drawn by these locomotives from London to Plymouth is 45 tons in excess of that allowed by the powerful and speedy "Castles." I think I ought to make it clear, however, that the increase in maximum loads does not in itself indicate the real extent of the increased power, as operating speeds have also been improved.

This table gives some of the maximum loads laid down for passenger trains between Paddington and Plymouth:

Class of engine.	Paddington to Taunton and back.	Taunton to Plymouth and back.
4-6-0 "Kings"	500 tons.	360 tons.
4-6-0 "Castles"	455 ,,	315 ,,
4-6-0 "Stars"	420 ,,	288 ,,
4-6-0 29XX, 2-6-0 43XX }	392 ,,	252 ,,
4-4-0 "Counties"	364 ,,	230 ,,
4-4-0 "Bulldogs"	336 ,,	200 ,,

The "King" engines are now employed on a number

of the principal express services and their use will doubtless be considerably extended as the fleet increases.

You will be glad to know that the Great Western Railway Company is already more than satisfied with the performances of the " Kings " and that the new engines have not only enabled traffic requirements to be met more expeditiously, but also with economy in running costs. All this, of course, spells efficiency.

Now first of all I think we will try to trace the evolution of the " King " class of locomotives stage by stage from the earliest types. In doing so we shall see how the power of the engines has developed and also how far the influence of the early designers is retained in even this latest development of locomotive engineering.

We ought also, I think, to have a talk about the building of these engines and try to follow the various processes of a " King " in the making. After that I should like to tell you something about " King George V " in America; and then . . . but that is, perhaps, enough for the moment.

Dignity and Impudence. A Swindon contrast.

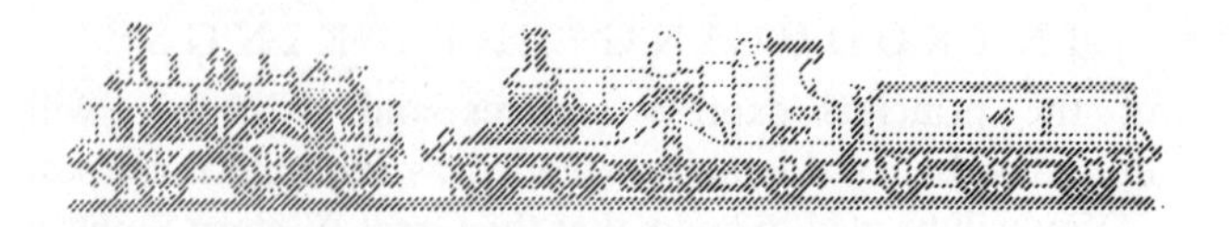

CHAPTER THE SECOND

THE EVOLUTION OF THE "KINGS"

THE SINGLE-WHEELERS

THE "King" class of G.W.R. engines boasts a noble and distinguished ancestry, and the evolution of these super-locomotives may be traced back to "North Star," one of the first engines delivered to the Company. Many of the characteristic features of "North Star" will be found in locomotives performing useful service to-day.

We have it on the authority of Daniel Gooch, the first locomotive superintendent of the Great Western Railway, and who, by the way, was appointed to that responsible position when but twenty-one years of age, that "North Star" was the best of the engines supplied to the Company in its earliest days, and used at the opening of the line in June 1838. His diary reads: "The 'North Star' being the most powerful one and in other respects the best, was my chief reliance."

It is interesting to remember that young Gooch had come to the Great Western Railway from Messrs. Robert Stephenson and Co. of Newcastle, and that it was whilst he was in the latter firm's service that "North Star" was designed.

THE EVOLUTION OF THE "KINGS"

Three days before the official opening of the railway, the first passenger train on the Great Western Railway was drawn by "North Star." It conveyed 200 passengers and attained a speed of 36 miles an hour.

This famous old engine, it should be noted, was unlike others acquired by the Company at that time, which had been built by the makers to the specific requirements of its engineer—the great Brunel—for his 7-ft. gauge railway. "North Star" had actually been constructed by Messrs. Robert Stephenson and Company for the New Orleans Railway of America, a line of 5 ft. 6 in. gauge and, with a sister engine "Morning Star," was thrown on to the makers' hands owing to a panic which came over the commercial world about this time. Fitted with larger driving wheels, at the request of Brunel, and adapted for his broad gauge, "North Star," when delivered to the Great Western Railway, was as shown in this photograph, which is of the full-sized model reconstructed at Swindon in connection with the Railway Centenary celebrations held at Darlington in 1925.

At this point, perhaps, a digression is permissible. For some unaccountable reason—and it seems hardly forgivable—"North Star" was broken up, but in connection with the Railway Centenary celebrations it was felt that an effort should be made to rebuild the old warrior. Some of the principal parts, including the crank axle and wheels, were discovered at Swindon Works—no one appears to have had the heart to scrap them. When the intention of reconstructing "North Star" became known, other of the original parts, including the name-plates and some of the buffers, were contributed. One of the buffers, it was found, was a treasured souvenir, and in use as a music-stool. It was really wonderful how so many pieces of the old engine came together.

The rebuilt " North Star " was a fellow-voyager with " King George V " when the latter was sent overseas last summer as an exhibit at the Baltimore and Ohio Railway

" North Star " as built in 1837.

Centenary " Fair of the Iron Horse," the two engines representing Great Western Railway locomotives ancient and modern. Thus " North Star " was actually despatched to America, for which country she was originally constructed, just ninety years late !

Besides furnishing an interesting link with those great railway pioneers, the Stephensons and Brunel, the rebuilt

" North Star " serves as a reminder of what was probably the greatest of all railway controversies, that which arose around Brunel's ambitious broad (7 ft.) * gauge and the narrow (now standard—4 ft. 8½ in.) gauge adopted by Stephenson.

And now to resume. It will be seen from the photo-

" North Star " as rebuilt in 1854.

graph that as originally built by Messrs. Robert Stephenson and Company " North Star's " boiler had a dome and two separate valves on the barrel. She had cylinders 15 in. diameter by 18 in. stroke, and was fitted with " Gab " motion. In 1854 the boiler was extended about 5 in., the dome removed, and the safety-valves combined and placed over the firebox. The cylinders were then increased to 16 in. in diameter, and in the altered condition

* Actually 7 ft. 0¼ in.

(shown in this photograph) " North Star " gave good service until 1870, having covered 429,000 miles in her 32 years of active life with the Great Western Railway.

When ordering the engine from his friend Robert Stephenson, Brunel concluded his letter with the remark, " . . . And I look forward to having such an engine as never was before." " North Star " was duly delivered to the Company at Maidenhead, to which point it was conveyed from Newcastle by water, and later Brunel wrote " . . . . We have a splendid engine of Stephenson's, it would be a beautiful ornament in the most elegant drawing-room."

It has been truly said that " North Star " was one of the most celebrated locomotives in the world, and this statement is justified by the fact that when she appeared she was the most powerful locomotive extant. If you compare the photograph with any of the illustrations of George Stephenson's " Locomotion No. 1 " you will appreciate the really wonderful progress which had taken place in the short space of twelve years since the latter had astonished the world at the opening of the Stockton and Darlington Railway. " North Star " probably had more effect upon railway locomotive design in this and other countries than any other engine for a great number of years.

So well had " North Star " shaped, as compared with some of the other engines supplied, that in 1839 ten similar locomotives were ordered from Messrs. Stephenson; and the standard passenger engines of the " Firefly " class, which were built later (1840–42), were essentially of the same type. This photograph is of " Acheron," one of the " Firefly " class.

It is interesting to notice that the boiler pressure in these early engines was between 50 and 55 lb. per square inch, or about one-fifth that of the " King " class of to-day. In the case of " Ixion," however, one of the engines of this batch, the boiler pressure was increased to 75 lb. per square inch for the purpose of preparing evidence for the Gauge Com-

" Acheron," one of Gooch's standard Passenger Engines of 1840–2. " Firefly " Class.

mission of 1845. Some of the devices adopted by the rival parties in the " Battle of the Gauges " were more amusing than ingenuous, for although the primary object of the locomotive trials was to determine the thermal efficiencies of the respective engines, neither side was averse to filling the tanks with hot water. It is even said that the narrow gauge exponents, who appear to have been both zealous and resourceful, made use of a stationary steam plant to liven up the engine fire after each trip! This would hardly appear to support the maxim as to honesty being the best policy, for, as is well known, the narrow gauge party was ultimately triumphant.

The next stage in the evolution of the G.W.R. passenger locomotive was the production at Swindon in 1846 of Gooch's famous engine, "Great Western." Incidentally she was the first locomotive entirely built at Swindon Works and a wonderful achievement at that time, for design and construction together only occupied the incredibly short time of thirteen weeks!

There is little doubt that "Great Western" was built in anticipation of some renewal of the Gauge War. She was larger and more powerful than any locomotive then running, and was the prototype of what was destined to become a far-famed line of 8 ft. single-wheeler engines. The boiler pressure was increased to 100 lb. per square inch and with the larger driving wheels the cylinders were proportionately increased, being of 18 in. diameter and 24 in. stroke. As in previous classes the firebox was of the Gothic or "haystack" type. Originally six-wheeled (2–2–2), it was later found necessary to add a second pair of leading wheels on account of the great weight carried at the front end of the engine.

"Great Western" was an outstanding success and in June 1846 she covered the 77¼ miles from Paddington to Swindon with a load of 100 tons in 78 minutes, or at the average speed of 59·4 miles an hour. A further 29 engines were put in hand between 1847 and 1855, the only alteration being that the boilers were of the round-top firebox type. Known as the "Iron Duke" class these engines earned a great reputation for speed. A famous representative of the class, "Great Britain," covered the 53 miles between Paddington and Didcot at the extraordinary average speed of 67 miles an hour, and it was during some experiments with three of these engines that 78 miles an hour was recorded on the Dauntsey incline.

Possibly the most renowned of the class was "Lord of

"Lord of the Isles."

the Isles." Built in 1851 she was continuously in service until 1884 with her original boiler intact and during that time ran 789,000 miles. "Lord of the Isles" was the first G.W.R. locomotive to be exhibited in America and, besides being on view at the Chicago Exhibition in 1893, was shown at the Great Exhibition of 1851, the Edinburgh Exhibition of 1890, and the Earl's Court Exhibition of 1897. She was broken up at Swindon in 1906. This photograph of "Lord of the Isles" shows the seat for the "travelling porter" on the tender facing the train. The duty of the occupant was to warn the driver if anything happened to the train. Supporters of the narrow gauge made capital out of this by facetiously referring to this porter as "the man in the iron coffin," who was placed on the tender to give notice of the many dangers to which passengers on the broad gauge were exposed!

Now carefully compare the photographs of the original "North Star" and "Lord of the Isles" and you will, I think, agree that the latter is a development of the Stephenson design.

The year 1855 witnessed the advent of the narrow gauge locomotive on the Great Western Railway, eight such engines (numbered 69 to 76) being constructed to Gooch's designs by Messrs. Beyer and Peacock of Manchester in that year. They were the first locomotives built by this firm and retained the slotted sandwich frames which were a feature of the Stephenson engines.

First employed on the Birmingham and Chester services, these engines were subsequently put on the Paddington to Birmingham run. Between 1872–75 they were reconstructed with larger cylinders and boilers at Wolverhampton, and being stationed at Swindon, worked the South Wales and London trains until 1897, when they were converted to four-coupled engines and named after English rivers.

Ten engines of 2–2–2 type were built by Messrs. Sharp, Stewart and Co. in 1862, and for some time worked the northern expresses between Paddington and Wolverhampton. They were numbered 157 to 166. Proving rather light for the work upon which they were engaged, however, they were subsequently replaced by Swindon-built engines carrying the same numbers.

In 1864 Gooch was succeeded as Locomotive Superintendent of the Great Western Railway by Mr. Joseph Armstrong. Here it should be remarked that Mr. Daniel Gooch became Chairman of the Great Western Railway in November 1865 and was created a baronet in the following year. Two years after Mr. Armstrong's appointment there appeared the first of thirty 7 ft. single-wheeler engines named, as a compliment to the Company's first Locomotive

" Cobham " (157–166 Class).

Superintendent, the " Sir Daniel " class. These engines were on express services until about 1895, and in 1902 a somewhat curious transformation took place in the conversion of twenty-one of the class to 0–6–0 type with 5 ft. driving wheels.

The next step was the production in 1873 of No. 55, " Queen," which was appropriately employed for several years in hauling royal trains. Twenty engines very similar in design were constructed in 1875 and, with certain modifications, were used for express services up to the close of the century, part of their work being the 120½ miles run from Paddington to Worcester, which was performed in 2 hours 16 minutes.

In 1876 Mr. Armstrong was succeeded by Mr. William Dean who, three years after his appointment, replaced the Sharp Stewart engines by some handsome locomotives in which the slotted sandwich frames reappeared. He also built two 7 ft. 8 in. single-wheelers in 1884 and 1886 (Nos. 9

" Queen."

and 10), the former of which was remarkable for the outside position of its links and eccentrics—a unique feature in those days. The driving wheels were reduced to 7 ft. in 1890, when the outside eccentrics of No. 9 disappeared.

The first of a famous series of eighty single-wheelers appeared in 1891, eight being constructed for the broad gauge and converted to the narrow in 1892, the year of the abolition of the " 7-ft. way." These and twenty-two more engines were built as 2–2–2's, with 20 in. by 24 in. cylinders but, as the result of a derailment in the Box

Tunnel, they were rebuilt with leading bogies, the cylinders being reduced to 19 in. by 24 in. The remaining fifty engines were similarly constructed.

Now we come to the end of the single-wheeler era, for no single driving wheel engines were built for the Great Western Railway after the year 1899. It is, however, little short of remarkable that, despite the low adhesion of all "singles" and the ever-increasing traffic demands, the "North Star" type of locomotive should have been per-

"Bessemer." Broad gauge 7 ft. 8 in. single-wheeler, as built in 1891.

petuated in all its essential features right down to the close of the nineteenth century.

The early history of the Great Western Railway is punctuated with wonderful speed records by these old single-wheelers, and there are many remarkable achievements credited to the famous 7 ft. 8 in. singles, of which none is more noteworthy than the final portion of the run by an Ocean mails special from Plymouth to Paddington in May 1904. From Bristol the train was hauled by No. 3065 "Duke of Connaught," and the time for the 118 miles 33 chains from Pylle Hill, Bristol, was 99 minutes 46 seconds, the final 77¼ miles from Swindon to London being accomplished in 19 seconds under the hour!

Here is a table which summarises some of the principal features of the single-wheeler era:

" Achilles." Narrow gauge 7 ft. 8 in. single-wheeler, built as 4–2–2 type in 1894.

THE "SINGLE-WHEELERS"

Class	Date built	Type	Cylinders	Diameter of driving wheel		Boiler pressure (lbs. 1 sq. inch)	Heating surface (sq. ft.)	Grate area (sq. ft.)	
			ins.	ft.	in.				
"North Star" .	1837–41	2–2–2	15 × 18	7	0	50	711	—	"North Star" re-built in 1854 with 16″ × 18″ cylinders.
"Firefly" . . .	1840–2	2–2–2	15 × 18	7	0	50–55	648	—	16″ × 20″ cylinders at a later date.
"Iron Duke" . .	1846–55	4–2–2	18 × 24	8	0	110–115	1,790	21·6	
157–166 . . .	1855	2–2–2	15½ × 22	6	6	—	1,112	13·6	
"Sir Daniel" . .	1866–69	2–2–2	17 × 24	7	0	—	1,269	16·75	
"Queen" . . .	1873–5	2–2–2	18 × 24	7	0	140	1,279	18·0	
157–166 . . .	1878–9	2–2–2	18 × 24	7	0	140	1,214	19·3	
3001–3080 . . .	1891–7	4–2–2	19 × 24	7	8	160	1,445	20·8	3001–3030 were originally built as 2-2-2's with 20″ × 24″ cylinders.

CHAPTER THE THIRD

THE EVOLUTION OF THE "KINGS"

FOUR-WHEELS COUPLED

ALTHOUGH the building of "single-wheelers" was carried on up to the closing years of the nineteenth century, the four-wheels coupled engine had been introduced early in the Company's history for passenger work entailing heavy loads or severe gradients.

As far back as 1849 Gooch had designed the first of his "Bogie" class locomotives, which were saddle-tank 4–4–0's built specially for the heavy gradients on the South Devon Railway. The construction of these engines was peculiar in that the boiler formed the connecting link between the cylinders and the main engine frame.

In 1855 ten eight-wheeled four-coupled engines with 7 ft. diameter driving-wheels and cylinders 17 in. by 24 in. were built for the Company by Messrs. Robert Stephenson and Company. Known as the "Waverleys," these locomotives were intended for express passenger work, but on account of their long rigid wheel base, they were not really suitable for such duties and they gave place to the "Victoria" class (2–4–0) which had 6 ft. 6 in. driving-wheels and cylinders 16 in. by 24 in. Here is a photograph of "Waverley," which has, as you see, the travelling porter's seat on the tender.

We cannot do more than mention Gooch's Metropolitan tank condensing engines of 1862, or his "England" class of 2–4–0 type which had 6 ft. 6 in. drivers and cylinders 16 in. by 24 in., but must pass on to twenty-six engines of the "Hawthorn" class built in 1865–66 with 6 ft. driving wheels. These were later converted to 2–4–0 saddle-tank

"Waverley," built in 1855.

type with 5 ft. wheels for service in South Devon and Cornwall. Some of them ran until the abolition of the broad gauge in 1892.

Large numbers of four-coupled passenger tank locomotives were built between 1869 and the end of the century. Those constructed at Swindon were mainly 2–4T–0's, whilst those built at Wolverhampton were chiefly of 0–4T–2 type. The majority of these engines had 5 ft. coupled wheels and cylinders 16 in. by 24 in. They were employed on the slower passenger trains.

From about the same time a large number of 2–4–0 tender

engines for passenger service were built at Swindon. The first of these, numbered 439–444, were to Mr. Armstrong's designs of 1868 and had 6 ft. coupled driving wheels and cylinders 16 in. by 24 in. Among the last of this type to be built were Mr. Dean's famous "Barnums." The first of this latter class came out in 1889 and had 6 ft. 1½ in. coupled drivers and cylinders 18 in. by 24 in. It is particularly interesting to notice that in this type the slotted outside frames of the "North Star" design were again repeated.

"Barnum" Class.

This photograph of No. 3221 demonstrates how the influence of early types has been maintained for nearly sixty years. In later lots (1892–93) the diameter of the driving wheels was increased to 6 ft. 6 in. and that of the cylinders was reduced to 17½ in., the outside framing being retained for the leading wheels only. These engines were employed on express passenger services.

A new class of four-coupled passenger engines was brought out by Mr. Dean in 1894, of which only four were built.

They had 7 ft. coupled wheels, 20 in. by 24 in. cylinders and a leading bogie, but were soon found unsuited to the express work for which they had been designed. Nos. 7 and 8 were

No. 14 Broad-gauge Convertible, built in 1888.

rebuilds of Mr. Dean's experimental tandem compound engines bearing those numbers, and the other two engines of the class—Nos. 14 and 16—were first built as convertible

No. 14 as rebuilt in 1894—" Charles Saunders."

broad-gauge engines of the 2-4-0 type. The engines were named " Armstrong," " Gooch," " Charles Saunders " (the first secretary of the Company) and " Brunel " respectively, after great men who had played prominent parts in the early history of the Railway.

Prior to 1895 the express passenger services over the heavy gradients of South Devon and Cornwall had been worked by 5 ft. coupled engines, some of which were conversions of broad gauge 0–4T–2 type engines built for the narrow gauge as 0–4T–4's. This photograph is of No. "3548." In 1895, however, Mr. Dean designed and built 4–4–0 type engines specially for this service. Known as

No. 3548, used on South Devon services before introduction of "Duke" Class.

the "Dukes" and "Devonshires" they had 5 ft. 8 in. diameter coupled wheels, 18 in. by 26 in. inside cylinders and round top boilers carrying a pressure of 160 lb. per sq. in. The leading bogie of this class was similar to that which Mr. Dean employed for his carriage stock, and the wheels of both bogie and tender had wooden centres. These engines were so successful that Mr. Dean produced a similar class for hauling heavy express trains on long stretches of level or moderately graded roads. These were the " Badmintons " and carried boilers with a Belpaire type firebox and had coupled wheels of 6 ft. 8½ in. diameter, a favourite dimension for express locomotives

No. 3252, " Duke of Cornwall," with wooden bogie and tender wheels.

for many years. The wheels of both bogie and tender were of the usual spoke pattern, the wooden wheels of the earlier " Dukes " not being repeated after 1897.

No. 3292, " Badminton."

You will see by this photograph of No. 3292 " Badminton " how design was developing towards the modern type.

Both " Duke " and " Badminton " classes were later

No. 3717, " City of Truro."

modified by the addition of large boilers, and thus we get the "Bulldog" class of 1898 (aptly named, for they conveyed an impression of strength and tenacity not before introduced), and the "Atbara" class of 1900, respectively. Both types again appeared with the building in 1909 of the "Bird" and "Flower" classes.

Mr. G. J. Churchward succeeded Mr. Dean in 1902, and in the following year produced his famous "City" class of 4–4–0 type tender engines with 6 ft. 8½ in. coupled wheels and inside cylinders 18 in. by 26 in. Mr. Churchward discarded the dome on the boiler and also dispensed with the use of a perforated pipe for collecting the steam, as the great height of the boiler above the firebox enabled dry steam to be taken without the necessity of either dome or perforated pipe.

The "Cities" were remarkable for their speed and it was one of this class, No. 3440 "City of Truro," which attained the highest authentic speed in the history of railways (102·3 miles an hour) when hauling an Ocean Mails Special from Plymouth to Bristol in May 1904.

We next come to the "County" class, a 4–4–0 type passenger engine of new design with 6 ft. 8½ in. coupled driving wheels and outside cylinders 18 in. by 30 in., which appeared in 1904. By the addition of a trailing radial truck and the provision of tanks and coal bunker in place of tender we get the "County" tanks of a year later. These latter engines (4–4T–2) were largely employed on suburban express services for which they were particularly suitable, as they did not require to be turned round at the end of each trip. Here are photographs of No. 3473, "County of Middlesex," and No. 2230, County Tank.

With the exception of some "Atlantic" (4–4–2) engines, afterwards converted to six-coupled passenger engines (to which class they properly belong), the "County" was

No. 3800, "County of Middlesex."

the last class of four-coupled engines to be designed on the Great Western Railway. It is perhaps not a little strange that the line which so reluctantly abandoned the old "single-

No. 2230, County Tank.

wheeler" in favour of the four-coupled engine, should so soon have displaced the latter by its more powerful rival, the six-coupled engine.

The more important features of some of the four-coupled engines we have mentioned will be found in this table.

FOUR-COUPLED PASSENGER ENGINES

Class	Date built	Type	Cylinders	Diameter of driving wheel	Boiler pressure (lbs. 1 sq. inch)	Heating surface (sq. ft.)	Grate area (sq. ft.)	
			ins.	ft. ins.				
"Bogie" . . .	1849	4–4T–0	17 × 24	6 0	—	—	18·4	Later engines built in 1854–55 with 5′ 9″ wheels.
"Waverley" . .	1855	4–4–0	17 × 24	7 0	—	1,574	19·2	
"Barnum" . .	1889	2–4–0	18 × 24	6 1½	150	1,469	19·0	
"Duke" . . .	1895	4–4–0	18 × 26	5 8	160	1,398	19·0	Fore-runner of "Bull-dog" and "Bird" classes.
"Badminton" .	1897	4–4–0	18 × 26	6 8½	180	*951	18·3	* Boiler fitted with "Serve" tubes. Fore-runner of "Atbara" and "Flower" classes.
"City" . . .	1903	4–4–0	18 × 26	6 8½	195	1818	20·6	
"County" . .	1904	4–4–0	18 × 30	6 8½	200	1,818	20·6	

N.B.—The particulars given are as locomotives were first built.

CHAPTER THE FOURTH

THE EVOLUTION OF THE "KINGS"

SIX-WHEELS COUPLED

THE opening years of the twentieth century witnessed a rapid growth in passenger traffic on the Great Western Railway. Train loads were increasing and, with the existing types of locomotives, it was frequently necessary to utilise banking engines on the steeper gradients on the main line to the west of England. Now, as you know, that is not quite the G.W.R. way of doing things. The assistance of banking engines was chiefly required with the heavier express passenger trains with the result that not only were some delays necessitated, but the best use could not be made of the available engine power, as the banking, or assistant, engine was only required for one or two additional coaches over the normal load.

It soon became apparent that if long " non-stop " runs were to be attempted, more powerful locomotives would be necessary and so we find that, although the " single-wheeler " was not displaced from the proud position it held until the closing years of the nineteenth century, its immediate successor, the " four-coupled " engine, was

coupled engines and were subsequently allocated to less important services.

All three of these engines were eventually fitted with G.W.R. standard taper boilers, and in this form "La France" and "President" worked until 1926 and 1927 respectively, when they were cut up. "Alliance" is still in service.

The characteristic features of these engines were the divided drive—the inside cylinders driving the leading coupled axle, and the outside cylinders driving the second

No. 102, "La France."

or intermediate coupled axle; the use of separate valve gears for each pair of cylinders, enabling the point of cut-off to be varied independently in each, so obtaining maximum efficiency under all conditions of working; and the use of an intercepting valve by which live steam could be admitted to both cylinders so as to give augmented power for starting or climbing gradients with a heavy load.

Now you will probably remind me that these engines were of the four-coupled class, whereas we are considering the locomotive with six coupled wheels. That is perfectly true, but I have mentioned them here because their influence was principally felt in the design of the four-cylinder six-coupled engines which followed somewhat later.

In the meantime "Albion" (No. 171), a famous engine, had been built. She was somewhat similar to No. 98, but her boiler pressure had been raised to 225 lb. per square inch in order to be comparable with the 227·5 lb. per square inch of "La France." To make the working of the two engines even more comparable, "Albion" was converted to the 4–4–2 wheel arrangement, but with thirteen other engines so built, was later reconverted to 4–6–0 type. By

No. 171 (now No. 2971), "Albion."

that time it had been abundantly proved that six-coupled engines were equally free in running, besides having the advantage of increased adhesion.

The later two-cylinder 4–6–0 type engines carried a cone boiler tapering the whole of its length and the cylinders were increased from 18 in. to 18½ in. by 30 in.; the higher pressure of 225 lb. per square inch being retained. The outline of the framing was improved as can be seen from this photograph of "Tortworth Court" (No. 2955). A further development of this class took place with the substitution of 6 ft. driving wheels in the place of the original

6 ft. 8½ in. wheels, thus making the engine more suitable for hauling heavy loads over severe gradients. This

No. 2955, " Tortworth Court."

photograph is of " Saint Martin " (No. 2925), the first engine so altered.

No. 2925, " Saint Martin."

Whilst the compounding principle of the de Glehn engines was not adopted, the divided drive of the French engines was incorporated in the four-cylinder, 4–6–0 type, simple engine No. 40, " North Star " (named after the old broad-gauger), brought out in 1906. The cylinders were of 14¼ in. diameter by 26 in. stroke, those between the frames being placed ahead of, and those outside the frames behind, the bogie centre. The valve gear was unusual in that the gear on each side of the engine received the principal part of its motion from the crosshead on the opposite side, the

No. 40 (now No. 4000), the first G.W.R. four-cylinder locomotive, built as 4–4–2, but altered later to 4–6–0.

outside valves being driven from the inside gear by means of specially shaped rocker arms.

Engine No. 40, shown in this photograph, was originally built as a 4–4–2, but was subsequently rebuilt with the

No. 4041, "Prince of Wales."

4–6–0 wheel arrangement. Later four-cylinder engines of this class were all of the 4–6–0 type and the valve gear was modified by using an eccentric instead of taking the motion from the opposite crosshead. The first of these engines had $14\frac{1}{4}$ in. by 26 in. cylinders, but, commencing with " Prince of Wales " (No. 4041), subsequent engines had the cylinders enlarged to 15 in. diameter.

We must not omit a brief mention of engine No. 111, " The Great Bear," which, built in 1908, was the first " Pacific" class (4–6–2 type) tender engine to be constructed in this country and, indeed, was the only representative of the class in Great Britain for fourteen years. Owing to its weight " The Great Bear " was restricted to the London-Bristol services, and so in 1924 the engine was converted

No. 111, " The Great Bear," built as 4–6–2 ; later converted to " Castle " (4–6–0) type, and renamed " Viscount Churchill."

to 4–6–0, " Castle " class type, being renamed " Viscount Churchill " after the Chairman of the Great Western Railway.

In 1922 Mr. C. B. Collett succeeded Mr. Churchward as Chief Mechanical Engineer, and in the following year he produced the famous engine " Caerphilly Castle " having four cylinders 16 in. by 26 in., a correspondingly large boiler and a pressure of 225 lb. per square inch. The steam to the outside cylinders was supplied through an outside steam pipe passing through the side of the smokebox and the frames were lengthened enabling an extended cab, affording much better protection for the engine crew, to be provided. The tractive effort of these engines was 31,625 lb. at 85 per cent. boiler pressure, as compared with 27,800 lb. for the previous four-cylinder engines, thus making the "Castle" class the most powerful passenger locomotives in Great Britain at that time.

The next stage in passenger engine progress on the G.W.R. was the production of the wonder locomotives which are the subject of our talk. I have endeavoured to trace the development of the passenger locomotives of

No. 4073, "Caerphilly Castle"; first of the "Castle" Class, built in 1923.

the Great Western Railway from the earliest days—from the old "North Star" of 1837 to the "King George V" of 1927—and hope I have shown in this ninety years' review that the latest "King" class of engine is not only the product of her able designer and builder, but also of the accumulated knowledge of locomotive engineers throughout the railway era, and that in the latest engines can be traced the influence of the pioneers of locomotive construction.

Referring to the production of the "Kings" Mr. Collett has said:

My ambition was to follow, even if a very long way off,

SIX WHEELS-COUPLED ENGINES

Class	Date built	Type	Cylinders	Diameter of driving wheels	Boiler pressure (lbs. 1 sq. inch)	Heating surface (sq. ft.)	Grate area (sq. ft.)	
			ins.	ft. in.				
"William Dean" .	1902	4–6–0	18 × 30 (two)	6 8½	200	2,410	27·62	
"Albion"	1903	4–6–0	18 × 30 (two)	6 8½	225	2,143	27·07	Converted to 4-4-2 in 1904. Reconverted in 1907.
"North Star" . .	1906	4–4–2	14¼ × 26 (four)	6 8½	225	2,143	27·07	Converted to 4-6-0 type in 1909.
"Prince of Wales"	1913	4–6–0	15 × 26 (four)	6 8½	225	2,104	27·07	
"Caerphilly Castle"	1923	4–6–0	16 × 26 (four)	6 8½	225	2,312	30·28	
"King George V"	1927	4–6–0	16¼ × 28 (four)	6 6	250	2,514	34·3	

very humbly in the footsteps of the great George Stephenson . . . at a meeting of the Institution of Mechanical Engineers in London a little while ago the Chairman remarked that the "Castle" engines in use on the Great Western Railway were just like George Stephenson's. I do not think he meant that for praise, but to my mind he could not have paid us a greater compliment, and I hope and trust that the engines of the new "King" class will prove to be also just as if George Stephenson had built them.

The principal stages of development in six-wheels coupled locomotives are shown in this table, which brings us up to date and, with the tables of the "single-wheelers" and four-wheels coupled locomotives, briefly summarises Great Western Railway passenger locomotive history.

CHAPTER THE FIFTH

"KINGS" IN THE MAKING

THE ENGINE PARTS

Now for a chat about some of the principal parts of the "King" locomotives, after which we will try and follow the processes of assembling them. Perhaps we had better divide our subject into "the engine parts" and "the boiler." I have some diagrams and photographs here which will be helpful in following the various descriptions.

CYLINDERS

First and foremost come the cylinders in which the energy latent in the steam is converted into work. In the "King" class, the cylinders comprise three separate castings. The two inside cylinders are combined with a saddle supporting the smokebox to form one casting, and the two outside cylinders are cast separately. The steam chests are embodied in their respective cylinder castings and passages are provided in both the outside and inside cylinders for tapping off a certain proportion of the exhaust steam for use in working the exhaust steam injector.

Take a good look at this photograph which gives us a front view of an engine under construction showing the arrangement of the cylinders. This will give you a better idea than the most wordy description.

The cylinders are cast from a specially selected close-grained iron, as hard as can be satisfactorily worked. The castings have to be free from blowholes, porous places, and all other defects. The cupola, in which the iron is melted, is a vertical brick-lined furnace which is charged, from a platform near the top, with alternate layers of coke, limestone, and a mixture of pig iron and "scrap," the latter being obtained by breaking up old cylinders.

With the aid of a forced draught, produced by a powerful blower capable of forcing 30,000 cubic ft. of air per minute against a pressure of 20 in. of water, the combustion of the coke produces a heat sufficient to melt the iron, which

Moulding Boxes for inside cylinders with upper portion removed.

trickles to the bottom of the cupola, ready to be tapped off through a small hole normally kept sealed by means of a fireclay plug. The limestone acts as a flux and unites with any impurities to form a slag which floats on the surface of the molten mass.

The iron is drawn off from the cupola into huge ladles,

from which it is poured into the moulds. To make the moulds, wooden patterns of the cylinders are embedded in special sands contained in strong iron boxes, and the mould left when the pattern is withdrawn is filled with the molten metal.

When pouring the metal, the bores of the cylinder, steam

Inside cylinder casting and casting of 18 in. × 30 in. outside cylinder.

chest, etc., are taken up by " cores " which have to be broken up and removed from the casting when completed. For such a casting as the combined inside cylinders and saddle, no less than twenty cores are required and the moulding box has to be built in four separate portions. These photographs show the moulding box with the top portion removed and the finished casting together with one of an outside cylinder engine.

A shop at Swindon Works is set aside for the machining and fitting of cylinders. The sides have to be carefully planed, as has also the radiused face of the smokebox saddle. The steam chests are bored to receive the piston valve bushes in a special machine, which deals with all four of the inside cylinder bushes at the same time, thus effecting

Machine boring steam chest.

a considerable saving. Here is a photograph of the machine in action. The bores of the cylinders and piston valve bushes are brought to their finished dimensions in a large grinding machine. A battery of machines for drilling and tapping the various bolt and stud holes is also included in the equipment of the cylinder-machining shop, and you may be interested to know that its approximate output of cylinders is 262 pairs per annum.

MAIN FRAMES

The main frames of the engines are received from the steel makers in the form of long rectangular slabs some 41 ft. 4 in. in length, by 3 ft. 6 in. in width, and $1\frac{1}{4}$ in. thick. These are first of all roughly punched to shape

Locomotive Frame Slotting Machine.

and, after annealing and levelling, are assembled in lots of eight or ten and machined to the finished dimensions in a slotting machine as you see in this photograph. The frames are next "dished" at the leading end in powerful hydraulic presses so as to provide the necessary clearance for the movement of the leading wheels of the bogie. They are subsequently assembled in pairs for drilling.

PISTONS

The piston head is a hollow iron casting of the "box" type, and is secured to the piston rod by a tapered screw thread and dowel which, though difficult to separate for renewal, preserves a flat face to the front of the piston head and thus enables the cylinder cover to be of strong and simple design. Steam-tightness is secured by fitting the

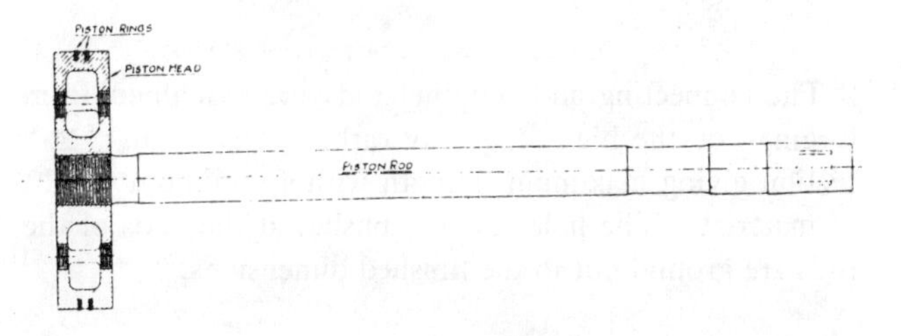

piston head with two piston rings which expand evenly against the cylinder walls as in a motor-cycle engine. The width of the rings is a matter of great importance as, if too wide, they are difficult to keep steam-tight; whilst, if too narrow, they wear quickly and tend to score the cylinder. The piston rod is kept steam-tight in passing through the back cylinder cover by means of a stuffing box and gland. Three or four turns of a flexible metallic packing covered with graphite paste are pressed into the stuffing box sufficiently tightly to prevent leakage of steam without scoring the rod.

CROSSHEADS

The crossheads are steel castings in which the slippers are incorporated. The faces of the slippers are lined with anti-friction metal held in position by means of corrugations in the face of the slipper. Bronze safety strips are let in so that, should the white metal get hot and run out no damage will be done. A 50-ton press is employed to force the crosshead on to the piston rod and a special broaching machine cuts out the hole for the cotter with the two units so assembled, thus securing perfect alignment.

CONNECTING AND COUPLING RODS

The connecting and coupling rods are machined from forgings of the highest quality carbon steel to an "I" section giving maximum strength with a minimum weight of material. The holes for the bushes at the ends of the rods are ground out to the finished dimensions.

AXLE BOXES

The driving axle boxes are steel castings into which are pressed gun-metal liners with white metal cast on the bearing surfaces. Oil is supplied to the horn cheeks and to the top of the journal by means of pipes leading from oil boxes carried on the frames, and fed to the bottom of the journal by pads saturated with oil and pressed against the journal by springs. This diagram, I think, makes it clear.

AXLES

The crank axle, on to which the inside cylinders drive, is built up from slabs and rolled bars. The slabs are planed

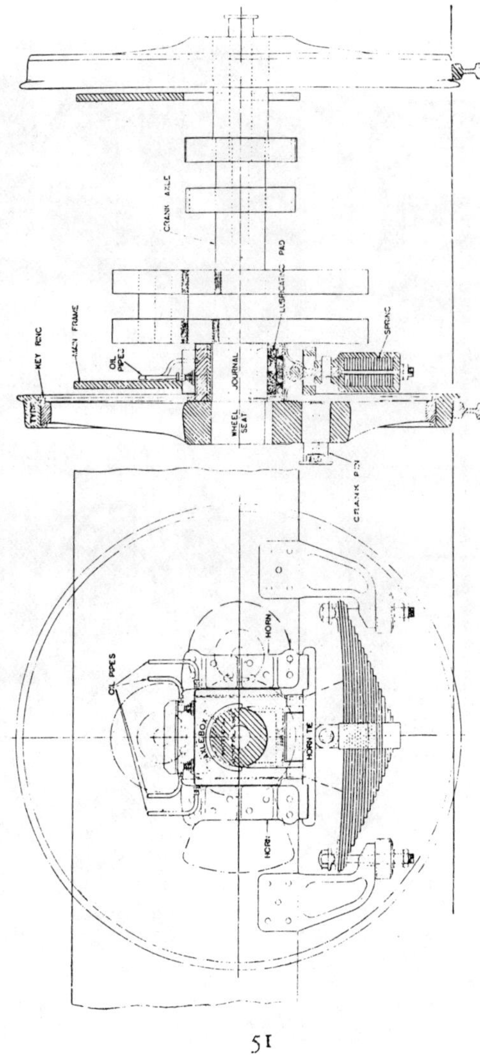

Diagram of Driving Wheel, Axle Box, etc.

Motion of "King" Class of Locomotives.

and bored to form the webs and are shrunk on to the bars, which are turned to form the crank pins and shaft. The

Built-up Balanced Crank.

other axles are straight, the crank pins for the outside cylinders being shrunk into the bosses of the intermediate driving wheels.

WHEELS

The wheel centres are of cast steel and are bored to receive the ends of the axles on to which they are forced with a hydraulic pressure of about 130 tons. This is a photograph of the duplex press in use. A tyre is bored somewhat smaller than the diameter of its wheel centre, and is heated in the gas furnace you see in the next picture by a series of gas jets until the diameter has increased to something greater than that of the centre. The tyre is then placed over the centre and allowed to shrink so that it grips tightly. A retaining ring is then hammered down between a lip on the tyre and the rim of the wheel centre

Duplex Hydraulic Press.

in order to hold the tyre in the remote possibility of it ever becoming loose.

Gas Furnace for heating tyres.

The wheels and axle are now taken to a wheel lathe and, after the tyre has been turned to the correct profile, the holes which receive the crank or coupling-rod pins are bored out in a quartering machine. This machine has two heads arranged at right angles so that both wheels can be bored simultaneously and at the correct angle. The wheels and

Wheel-quartering Machine.

axle finally go to a specially designed machine in which they are correctly balanced at speeds representing 60 miles per hour on the rail.

VALVE GEAR

I am afraid we cannot have more than a brief description of the valve gear, but this diagram will help to elucidate matters.

The piston valves for the inside cylinders are driven directly by Walschaerts' gear, which gives a motion compounded of two distinct movements. The principal movement is derived from an eccentric keyed to the axle,

Wheel-balancing Machine.

and the other movement from a connection taken from the crosshead. These two movements are conveyed one to each end of a combining lever from some intermediate point along which the valve derives its ultimate motion. This gear is adopted because of the relative lightness of its moving parts and its special suitability for high speeds.

The motion for the valves of the outside cylinders is derived from that of the inside by means of levers fulcrumed about pivots carried on the engine frames.

I am afraid that is brief indeed, but anything like an

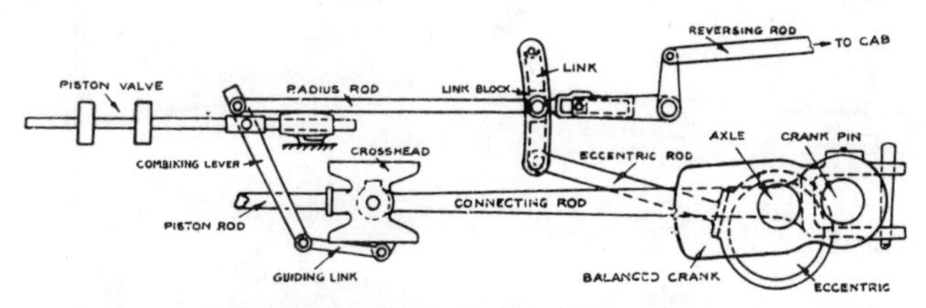

Diagram of Walschaërts' valve gear.

adequate treatise on valve gears would rob us of our beauty sleep and, quite frankly, the subject is one rather difficult to describe simply and in few words.

LUBRICATORS

We must mention the Swindon improved triple sight-feed lubricator—shown in this diagram—which distributes oil to the regulator (pipe S) and to the cylinders (pipe F). The oil contained in the lubricator is displaced through the sight-feed glasses by steam from the boiler condensing in pipes C. The feed to the cylinders is taken through D to a combining valve W. (I hope you can follow this.)

Here the oil is mixed with steam from the boiler and is carried along pipe F to the steam pipes in the smokebox

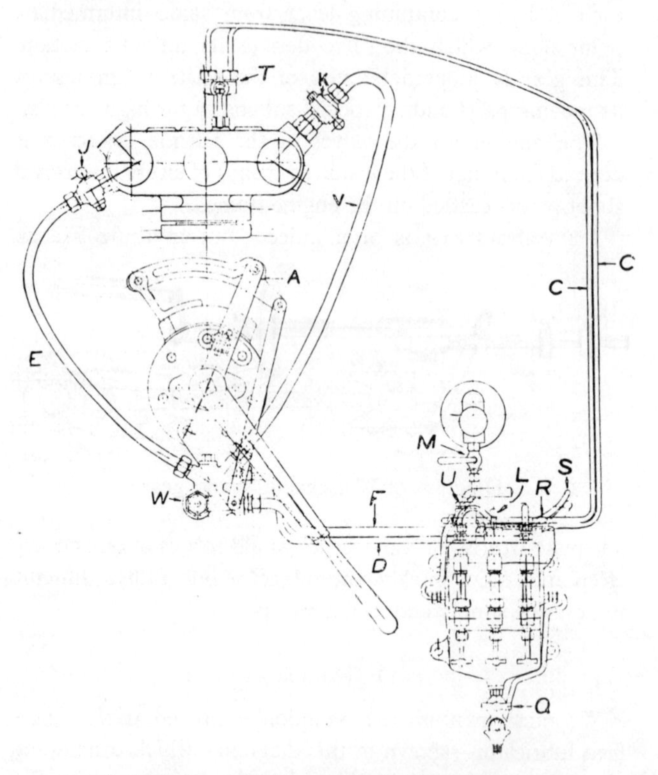

" Swindon " Triple Sight-Feed Lubricator.

and thence to the cylinders. Valve W, which is operated by moving the regulator handle, is so arranged that oil is fed to the cylinders when the engine is drifting (or

" coasting," to use a cycling term) and the regulator valve is shut.

So much then for the engine proper, and now we come to the unit which supplies the engine with steam—the boiler.

A Line of five " Kings."

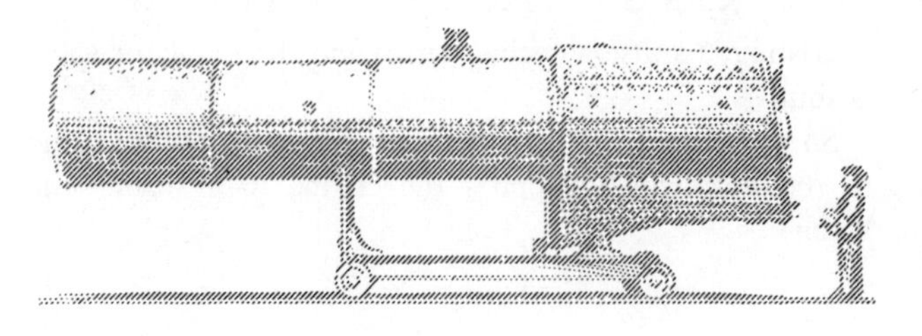

CHAPTER THE SIXTH

"KINGS" IN THE MAKING

THE BOILER

THE satisfactory working of a locomotive is, perhaps, dependent to a greater extent on the efficiency of its boiler than on any other part. The excellence of the Swindon product has long been a matter for justifiable pride

What are the requirements of a locomotive boiler? It must raise quickly and efficiently a sufficient volume of steam to meet all the working requirements of the engine. It must safely withstand a pressure considerably in excess of that at which it normally works, and every provision must be made for quick and thorough cleaning at frequent intervals so that the efficiency of the heat-transmitting surfaces remains unimpaired throughout their working life. With all this, it must conform to the restrictions of space imposed by the various structures met with on the railway and those of the engine frame upon which it is carried. Further, due regard must also be paid to the manner in which the total weight of the boiler is distributed over the wheels of the engine.

The characteristic feature of the G.W R. standard boiler is the coning of the barrel. Introduced in 1903 the coning was, as you have already been told, first restricted to the back barrel plate, but was later extended to the whole length of the barrel in order still further to improve the circulation of the water in the boiler. I have already explained how the tapering of the barrel enables the fullest

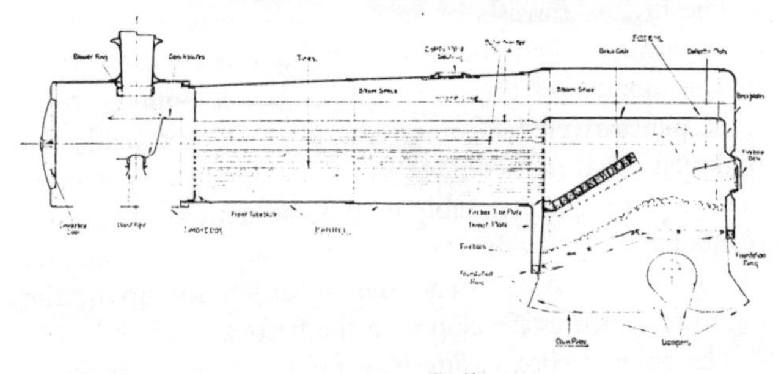

Locomotive Boiler.

Note : Superheater, Regulator Box and Gear, Safety Valve, Stays, etc. not shown.

use to be made of the intense heat in the neighbourhood of the firebox end, and how it minimises the danger of uncovering the firebox crown plates.

Steam is collected by means of an internal pipe with upturned mouths situated above the top of the front end of the firebox thus ensuring that dry steam only is taken to the regulator or main steam valve. This construction enables the latter to be placed in the smokebox, where it is readily accessible and obviates the need for a steam dome, which is such a familiar, if not very artistic, feature of many locomotives.

The boiler consists of three principal parts: the firebox, the barrel, and the smokebox. Let us take each in its turn, but before doing so you ought to have a good look at this drawing, which will assist you to follow the descriptions.

FIREBOX

The firebox consists of an inner box surrounded by an outer casing or shell, the two being connected at the bottom by the foundation ring. The inner box is built up from three plates riveted together, the front or tube plate, the back plate, and the wrapper plate. In English locomotive practice copper is invariably used on account of the greater resistance which it offers to the corrosive action of the fire, and its ability to withstand the distortion set up by the high temperatures developed in the firebox.

The outer firebox casing is of mild steel and consists of a throat plate, into which one end of the barrel is fitted; a back plate, flanged with the copper back plate to form the firehole; and a wrapper plate, which is usually in three portions, one crown and two side sheets, riveted together with butt strips.

BARREL

The barrel is built up from two mild steel plates rolled into butt-jointed circular rings riveted together with a circumferential lap joint. The front end is closed by a steel tube plate drilled to receive a large number of steel tubes, 2¼ in. in diameter, through which the hot gases pass on their way to the smokebox. The tubes are expanded into the tube plates in order to make them steam-tight and, where there is a risk of corroding deposits accumulating on the projecting ends, are beaded over to reduce the possibility of subsequent leakage.

SMOKEBOX

The smokebox is riveted to the end of the barrel and, with the door, which is of sufficient size to allow the tubes to be withdrawn or cleaned, forms an air-tight compartment through which the products of combustion are drawn on their way to the chimney.

After the steam has performed its useful work in the cylinders, it is exhausted through the blast pipe and chimney to the atmosphere. Some of the air contained in the smokebox is carried out with each jet of steam, and, to take its place, air flows in by way of the firebox and tubes. This produces the intense draught necessary for the consumption of the fuel. When starting or when working heavily on an ascending gradient, the volume of steam which is emitted from the blast pipe is so great that it would exert too fierce a pull on the fire, and so an automatic "jumper" top is fitted

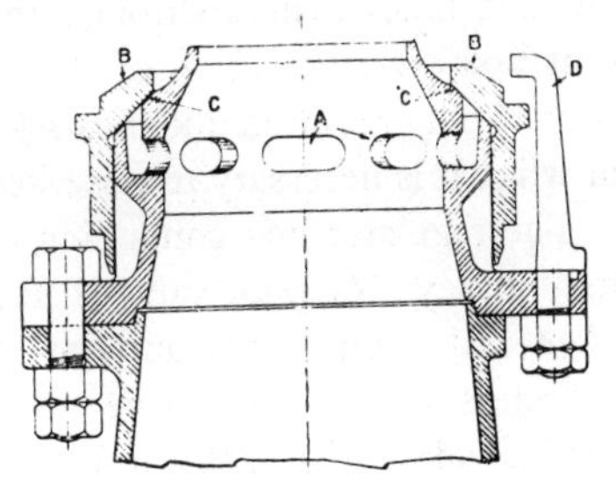

"Jumper" Blast Pipe Top.

When working heavily exhaust steam pressure lifts ring B, providing an extra outlet for exhaust through holes A and space between lifted ring B and its seat C. Lift of ring B is limited by stops D.

to the blast pipe. This "jumper" lifts when the exhaust exceeds a certain amount and provides an additional exit for the steam, thus softening the effect on the fire.

A spark arrester is fitted in the smokebox to induce an even draught through all the tubes, as, due to the position of the blast pipe top, there is a tendency for an excessive draught to be created through the top tubes. This plate gives the gases a downward trend, with the result that any ash drawn through the tubes is deposited in the bottom of the smokebox, so preventing sparks being thrown from the chimney.

At the base of the chimney is a combined blower and ejector exhaust ring. The blower portion directs live steam from the boiler up the chimney, through a series of inclined holes drilled through the inner wall of the ring, thus assisting the action of the blast. The blower is, of course, only required under exceptional running conditions, or when it is necessary to raise steam quickly in the shed.

The regulator box containing the main steam valve and its "jockey" or pilot valve is fixed at the top of the tube plate and controls the amount of steam admitted to the cylinders. The pilot valve not only permits of a very gradual admission of steam, but also facilitates the opening of the regulator as, with the full steam pressure acting on the valve, it is almost impossible to open the main valve directly.

The superheater is also located in the smokebox and consists of two chambers within one casting. Saturated steam—that is, steam in contact with the water from which it is produced—is picked up by the upturned mouths of the main steam pipe in the boiler and, passing through the regulator pipe, is then admitted to one chamber of the superheater header, from which it passes into the superheater tubes which are surrounded by hot gases. The steam is here superheated above the temperature of that in contact with the water and it returns to the other chamber of the header, from which it is distributed to the steam chest and cylinders.

CONSTRUCTION

Before leaving the subject of the boiler unit I should like to give you some idea of the method of construction of the locomotive boiler as followed at the Swindon Works.

Steel Throat Plate.

Hydraulic flanging of both steel and copper plates has always been a strong feature of Swindon practice and one of the first steps in boiler construction is the preparation of the blocks and dies with which the various shapes are pressed. The blocks are of cast iron and are machined to the finished dimensions so that it is unnecessary to correct the shape of the plates after pressing. A particularly good example of hydraulic flanging is that of the front casing or throat plate. This is made from $\frac{3}{4}$ in. mild steel plate and is pressed out to the finished form shown in this photograph in one heat. Reduction in the number of heats means not only economy in the cost of manufacture, but also a minimum of distortion in the material. Before being used

Hydraulic Press.

the blocks are warmed up in order to avoid any sudden chilling of the plate as the two come in contact.

Two presses are provided in the boiler shop ; the larger of the two (which you see in this photograph) deals with the heaviest classes of flanged plate work, while the smaller is used principally for flanging smokebox tube plates and for levelling smokebox rings. Operating at a pressure of

1,500 lb. per square inch, the larger press exerts a total pressure of 650 tons, and the other a pressure of about 200 tons.

The heating of the plates preparatory to pressing is carried out in either of two furnaces, the larger of which is coal fired and the other gas fired. The plates are manipulated mechanically when charging and discharging the furnaces with considerable saving in labour and time, besides enabling the work to be carried out with a minimum of physical discomfort to the workmen.

The copper plates used to be first heated and then flanged by beating up with wooden mallets, but this process has given place to flanging the cold plate by hydraulic pressure. The flanging of copper plates "in the cold" was first carried out successfully at Swindon Works and, besides being much cheaper than hand flanging, results in a big reduction in the number of plates with cracked corners.

After having been in the press, the rough-edged flanges of the steel plates are trimmed to the correct finished dimensions by an oxy-coal gas flame cutter. For this operation the plates are secured on a specially arranged table which can be adjusted to suit any of the standard plates. The copper plates are trimmed in horizontal band-sawing machines, the band-saw being supported in hardened steel guides carried on adjustable sliding brackets which permit of any sized plate being dealt with.

The barrel and wrapper plates are marked out to templates, the outline of the steel plates being cut out by a portable oxy-acetylene flame cutting machine. The stay holes in the crown plates are drilled, together with a few "tacking" holes along the seams, enabling the plates to be bolted together temporarily in assembling. Where one edge of a plate has to butt against another edge, such edges have to be carefully machined, and you will appreciate that very accurate work is required when, for example, the barrel plates are to fit one inside the other.

The copper and steel wrapper plates and the barrel plates are rolled to the correct shape in large bending rolls,

Copper wrapper plate in bending rolls.

three sets of which are used for rolling the plates and one for levelling them. Should the radius which it is desired to roll be smaller than that of the rolls themselves, use is then made of an auxiliary wooden roll placed between the main roll and the plate. The barrel plates are rolled conical throughout their length, but the ends require to be parallel as the rings fit one inside the other. The ends are therefore placed in a press consisting of a central block, the diameter of which is the exact internal diameter of the ring to be pressed, and a series of radial sectors which are pressed inwards with a force of 1,500 lb. per square inch. Here is a photograph of a copper wrapper plate in the bending rolls.

The inner firebox and the outer casing are separately

Copper Firebox set up on jig.

assembled on jigs, the plates being held together temporarily by means of the "tacking bolts" previously mentioned and which can be seen in this picture. These jigs can be adjusted to suit the varying heights and lengths of different fireboxes and, as you can see by the illustration, they incorporate an auxiliary feature in the shape of tubular legs which can be let down to support a platform upon which men may carry out work on the top of the box.

These photographs give two views of the firebox casing set up on a jig.

The rivet holes along the seams of the copper firebox are drilled while the box is still assembled on its jig, but the

Firebox Casing set up on jig.

outer casing is taken to a special drilling machine. The drilling head of this machine can be raised to any height while the table, to which the casing is secured, is capable of rotating through any angle and also of traversing in two directions at right angles to one another. With such a machine it is possible to drill the necessary holes however awkward may be the position. The next photograph shows the drilling machine at work on a firebox casing which you see resting on the rotating and traversing table.

The various plates are next riveted together, and in the illustration we see the outer casing being riveted in a powerful hydraulic machine working in conjunction with a crane capable of dealing with loads up to a maximum of 30 tons. Notice that the throat plate has been removed. This is done in order that the copper firebox, to which the foundation ring has now been temporarily secured, may be placed inside the casing.

Firebox Casing on jig—end view.

The foundation ring is of best Yorkshire iron, 4 in. by $3\frac{3}{4}$ in. in section, and has to be very accurately machined. The ring is set up on a large milling machine, to which it is secured by duplex jigs so that both the inside and the outside surfaces can be milled with only one setting on the table. The photographs show the ring in the milling machine and on the radial drill.

When the copper box is placed inside the casing the two are correctly lined up in their relative positions and temporarily secured by means of a few crown stays and bolts.

Firebox Casing on drilling machine.

Firebox Casing in hydraulic riveting machine.

Foundation ring in milling machine.

Foundation Ring being drilled on 8-ft. radial machine.

A master template, with numerous indentations forming points of support for the pointed end of a pneumatic portable drilling machine, is fastened along the centre line of the inside box and from this are drilled the stay holes, the drill passing right through the copper and steel plates in order to ensure perfect alignment. The holes are subsequently tapped ready to receive the large number of stays which are necessary to support the surfaces of the box.

This photograph gives a very good idea of the appearance of the finished firebox with the throat plate finally riveted in position. See what a tremendous amount of staying is necessary! The numerous small holes in the copper tube plate are those into which the ends of the small fire tubes are expanded, and the larger holes above them are those into which the ends of the tubes carrying the superheater units are expanded.

The barrel is now carefully lined up with the firebox, special gauges being used to ensure correct alignment both laterally and vertically. The two parts are temporarily held in position with a few "tacking" bolts before the throat plate connection is drilled ready for riveting in a powerful hydraulic machine having a gap 23 ft. in length, so that the whole boiler unit can be dealt with. An overhead crane, which lifts the boiler into position, is operated from the same platform as the riveting rams. Here are good photographs of the boiler suspended from its crane over the jaws of the hydraulic riveter and lowered between the jaws to complete the riveting around the "connection." Note the size of the boiler compared with the man.

The completed Firebox.

Boiler suspended over jaws of hydraulic riveter.

Boiler lowered between jaws of riveter.

" Foot "-stays and " palm "-stays, which are connected to the barrel of the boiler, are now put in and the smokebox tube plate is riveted in position. The tubes are inserted from the front end of the boiler and the front and back plates are secured by longitudinal steel stays before the boiler is handed over to the boiler mounters for the fitting of the regulator box, superheater, water gauges, safety valves, etc.

When completed, as you see it here, the boiler is tested

The completed Boiler.

under hydraulic pressure to 290 lb. per sq. in.—that is, 40 lb. per sq. in. above its working pressure. It is then further tested under steam to a pressure of 250 lb. per sq. in. The boiler now receives a coat of anti-corrosive paint before being handed over to the erecting shop ready for mounting on the engine frames. I ought to say that the smokebox is not *finally* secured to the barrel until the boiler has been tried in the frames, as the holes in the smokebox plate are marked off from those in the cylinder saddle casting.

BRICK ARCH

And now, even at the cost of being a little lengthy, we ought to have just a few words about the brick arch, firegrate, and ashpan. The first, as you will see from this little diagram showing the path of the gases through the boiler, extends in an upward direction from just below the bottom row of tubes in the firebox tube plate to about the middle of the firebox. It serves a twofold purpose as, by increasing the length of the passage of the gases, it enables

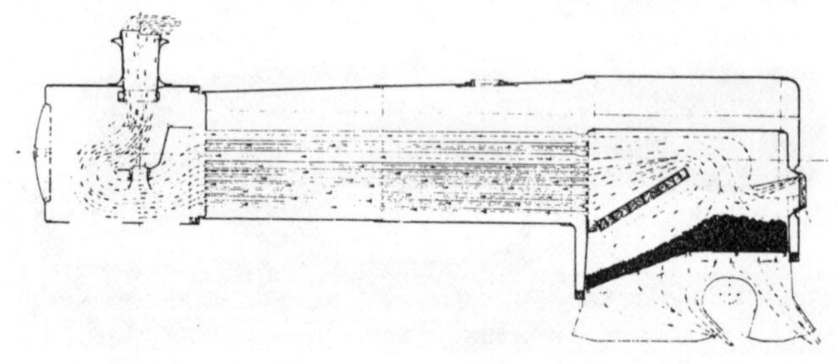

Gas Passages in Boiler.

complete combustion to take place before the gases leave the firebox and it also provides a reservoir of heat as the mass of firebrick becomes incandescent. To obtain complete combustion of the coal in the firebox some air must be allowed to enter over the top of the fire-bed and for this reason the firehole doors are cast hollow so that, even when shut, a warm current of air may be admitted. A deflector plate, fitted inside the firehole, prevents this additional air from impinging directly on the tube plate and thus causing leaky tubes.

FIREGRATE

The firegrate is arranged in sections, each consisting of a number of cast-iron firebars carried on transverse supports. Each bar is cast with lugs at the centre and ends which, acting as spacers, ensure that sufficient air space is provided. The front sections slope downwards towards the front of the firebox and, with the vibration of the engine, assist in getting the coal well forward.

ASHPAN

The ashpan, built up from $\frac{3}{16}$ in. steel plate, is secured to the bottom of the foundation ring and is made up in two portions so that, if necessary, it can be readily assembled over the trailing axle, which at this point is shielded from the heat of the fire by an asbestos lagging attached to the ashpan. The four doors provided can be opened or closed from the footplate, and their adjustment enables the amount of air admitted to the underside of the grate to be controlled.

We have devoted rather a lot of time to the boiler, but the excuse, if any is needed, is that it is such an essentially important feature. Anyway, you should now know something more about the boiler than the dear old lady who, associating the term with culinary operations, " supposed " it was necessary to make the locomotive *tender*.

And, after *that* I think we had better hurry on and, having considered the engine parts and the boiler, have a talk about their assembly.

CHAPTER THE SEVENTH

"KINGS" IN THE MAKING

ERECTING THE LOCOMOTIVES

To watch the building up, stage by stage, of a "King" locomotive—or any railway locomotive for that matter—and to see the various parts assembled in their respective places is both fascinating and instructive. We have here an excellent series of photographs which will help you to follow the sequence of operations from the laying of the frame plates to the production of the finished locomotive.

The frames as received from the machine shop are placed on low trestles with their inner faces uppermost, and on these inside faces are marked the more important locating lines, such as those for the centres of the inside cylinders, the inside motion plate, and the saddle casting—also those for the valve gear casting, auxiliary shaft bearings, frame cross-stays and drag box casting. The frames are then turned over so that their outer surfaces are uppermost, and these are marked with the centre lines for the outside cylinders, motion plates, and the box angle irons which support the footplate.

This done, the frame plates are lifted into a vertical position and mounted in adjustable forked stands, six being used for each plate, as it is important that the plates shall not sag under the weight of the many parts which are attached to them. Cross-stays, temporarily bolted into position, ensure that the frames are the correct distance apart.

The next step is to ensure that the frames are dead level both lengthwise and crosswise, and this is tested by means of a spirit level. Not only have the frames to be perfectly level, but also perfectly square, and, if necessary, one or other of the plates must be moved slightly until the diagonal distance between the centres of the leading horn on one side of the engine and of the intermediate horn on the other is the same, whichever pair of opposite horns is taken. "Centre-pop" marks are made on the top edge of the frame immediately above the centres of the horns and the diagonal distances between them are tried with long trammels.

The frames are now tested for straightness by trying them over with long straight-edges, and any portions which may be even slightly bent are lightly tapped on the concave face with a "knobbling" hammer while the opposite face is supported by holding a much heavier hammer against it. By this process the bent portions are drawn into line with the rest of the frame.

With the work so far properly squared and levelled it is possible to set up the trailing cheeks of the leading horns. These are the foundation from which other parts of the engine are set, so it is extremely important that these be

Main frames on trestles for marking out.

correctly fitted. The greatest care is exercised in keeping the cheeks both square and plumb. The front cheeks are set to the trailing cheeks by means of a " feeler," or gauge, thus ensuring that each pair is perfectly parallel.

The inside cylinders and motion plate can now be bolted temporarily in the frames, the correct position being obtained from lines passing through the bore of the cylinders, through the motion plate, and over a straight-edge so placed across the frames that one edge (that over which the string line passes) coincides with an imaginary line between the exact centres of the leading horns. Before the holes for the bolts which carry the cylinders and motion casting can be broached out to their finished

Two " Kings " under construction : that on right has the inside cylinders in position ; that on left has the outside cylinders fitted.

sizes, the cylinders and motion casting must be set so that they are absolutely central with the " lines," which must themselves be parallel with the top of the frames. The lines must also be at the correct distance from the cheeks of the leading driving horns, and these must be the correct gauge distance from the face of the cylinders.

The valve gear and saddle castings can now be tried in

the frames, and their positions determined from that of the inside cylinders. The holes for the carrying bolts are marked off, the castings are removed for drilling, again inserted in the frames (while the holes are broached out), and then temporarily bolted up in order to give the frames sufficient rigidity while the outside cylinders and motion plate are being fitted up. This latter process is very similar to that for the inside cylinders, lines being set through to a straight edge across the centres of the intermediate driving horns, and every care taken to ensure that they are square with the frames as well as central with the cylinders and motion plates. The cheeks of the intermediate driving horns are set from those of the leading driving horns, and here again the greatest care must be exercised in spacing the horns, for this determines the distance between the wheel centres which, in turn, must be rigidly adhered to, for the adoption of coupling rods with solid bushed ends does not permit of any adjustment afterwards. For similar reasons it is also essential that the face of the outside cylinders shall be the correct gauge distance from the intermediate driving horns, in this case due to the solid bushed ends of the outside connecting rods.

It is owing to the limitations of space with which the locomotive designer is continually confronted, that at this stage a little difficulty is encountered. A portion of the outside cylinders and the valve gear casting are in the same relative position on opposite sides of the frame with the result that, while some bolt holes pass through both the frame and castings, others are "blind." The valve gear casting is taken down while the outside cylinder holes are broached from the inside of the frame (the holes in the frame having been previously broached with the valve gear casting in position), and, after taking the cylinders down, the valve gear casting is finally secured with countersunk bolts. In this way the difficulty is overcome. The whole of the castings and cylinders can then be bolted up ready to be passed by an examiner.

I have dealt with these preliminary stages at some length, but I want you to appreciate the extreme care, accuracy, and precision which are essential in the erection of these powerful locomotives. . . . Now, I think, we can progress a little faster in erecting our engine.

With the various angle irons and stays riveted up and the framing practically complete, as much as possible of the motion work is erected before the boiler is dropped on the frames, since there are several details which would be exceedingly awkward to place after the boiler was in position. The inside cylinder covers are now fitted, together with the motion bars, reversing shaft and brackets, quadrants and auxiliary levers, brake cylinders and reservoirs, brackets and shafts; in fact anything which would prove difficult to get in if left till later on, is fixed at this stage.

Now the boiler can be tried on the frames, the smokebox being held loosely in position ready for marking off from the cylinder and saddle castings. The carrying brackets, which are attached to the firebox casing side plates, are carefully marked off so that not only is the boiler central with the frames transversely, but the centre line of the boiler is also parallel with the top line of the frames. Before finally securing the boiler, it is tried on a second time to check the smokebox holes, and to mark off on the underside

The Boiler being lowered between frames by 100-ton overhead cranes.

The Boiler in position ready for fixing to cylinder and saddle frames.

of the carrying bracket a groove to house the flat bearing springs which are interposed between the frame and bracket. Were it not for these springs (which are some 8 in. in length), it would be exceedingly difficult to secure an even distribution of weight on the frames with a firebox as long as that of the " King " engines.

Did you know that, whilst the boiler is firmly secured to the cylinder and saddle castings at the front end, it is

The Boiler covered with non-conducting composition.

necessary to make some provision for its expansion under working temperatures and that consequently the back end must be free to slide? Well, such is the case, the boiler being prevented from lifting at the back end by the provision of a bracket attached to the frames, which fits over the carrying bracket.

Nowadays the ashpan is fitted to the boiler before the

latter is " tried on," instead of assembling it separately over the trailing axle as was formerly the case.

Many parts are now added with a view to wheeling the engine. The axle boxes are fitted in the horns and bedded on the axles ; eccentric sheaves and straps are secured in position, and pistons, valves, crossheads, and air pump assembled. Oiling gear and all such fitments as the exhaust

The Engine lifted for wheeling : coupled wheels being run into position.

steam grease separator and injector pipe, which would be very difficult to fix after wheeling, are added, and the engine, ready for wheeling, is lifted off its supports by an electrically operated overhead crane capable of dealing with loads up to 100 tons.

The driving wheels are run underneath ready for the attached axle boxes to be guided into the horns as the engine is lowered on to them. Look carefully at the photograph and you will see that the front end of the engine is carried on screw jacks. These are to support the weight of the overhanging end until the bogie is placed in position.

Coupling and connecting rods are now erected, and valve gear and reversing gear coupled up ready for valve setting.

The Engine lowered on to the coupled wheels.

This operation is of great importance, for the successful running of the engine in service is largely dependent on the correct distribution of the steam to the cylinders. The frames are set to their normal running position and, while valve setting is proceeding, the front end of the engine is carried on a "dummy" bogie, as seen in the photograph, which enables the engine to be moved backwards and forwards as required.

The springs (if not already fitted), cylinder cock and brake gear, injector, cab, smokebox fittings, chimney, and the many other items which go to make the completed engine, may now be put in position. Our engine is rapidly taking final shape.

In the meantime, the boiler and cylinders have been coated with a non-conducting composition of magnesia

The Engine on a temporary bogie ready for valve setting.

and asbestos, and this, in turn, covered with thin sheet steel cleating plates. The ejector and hand rails are now fitted, and the painters get busy removing all dirt and grease and then applying a " priming " coat to all the surfaces which have to be painted. This is followed by a " working down " of the surfaces with " stopping," so obtaining an absolutely smooth surface with all hollows

Approaching completion : Cab plates fitted. Front of engine lifted to allow bogie to be fixed.

Bogie in position.

filled up. A coat of lead colour is next applied, followed by the finishing coats of green and the "lining out." The painted surfaces are then given one or more coats of varnish.

During painting our engine has been lifted at the front end and the bogie run under and secured in its correct position so that the engine can now be weighed and levelled at the correct running height. This weighing is carried out on an ingenious machine which shows simultaneously the weight on each wheel of the engine, and, by suitable adjustment of the springs, the total weight is correctly distributed over the whole wheel base.

Our "King" locomotive is now ready for a short trial run, during which it will be possible to see if the various parts are functioning properly, and to make any small adjustments that may be necessary. It will then be handed over to the Running Department at Swindon and employed for a short time on local trains so that any slight defect which may possibly develop can be corrected before being finally "passed out" for express passenger train working.

The "Kings," like other G.W.R. locomotives, are built for a long and useful life, which only really first-class workmanship throughout can ensure. One of the happiest of present-day writers has said of British humour, "Our jokes are like our locomotives: we take infinite pains in their design, material, and construction, and we expect them to last a lifetime. Usually we are not disappointed." There's a lot of truth in that. Anyway, here's a long life to the "Kings."

Five " Kings " in the making—in various stages of construction.

We are not the only folks who have taken an interest in the construction of the "Kings," and excursions to Swindon—"the birthplace of the 'King' locomotives"—have proved popular both from London and several of the larger provincial towns. You may be surprised to learn that between November, 1927, and June, 1928, about 50,000 persons participated in these special excursions to Swindon Works.

About 700 persons took tickets for the first excursion; in fact, so great was the demand that advanced booking had to be stopped some days before that fixed for the trip. The excursionists have been conducted over the G.W.R. Works at Swindon where they have seen the "King" and other classes of locomotives, besides railway carriages and wagons, under construction.

"King" locomotives have been appropriately employed to haul these excursion trains, and this feature has made them additionally attractive, particularly to the younger railway enthusiasts who have participated in such large numbers. Here is a jolly photograph of schoolboys from Cardiff expressing delight at the prospect of their trip to Swindon.

At Bristol a public-spirited citizen generously defrayed the cost of a special excursion to Swindon for 700 schoolboys of that City and the *Western Daily Press* offered prizes for the best essays written by the youngsters on their experience. Some of these compositions were good descriptive accounts of the journey out and home as well as of the various processes carried on at Swindon. The intelligent grasp of the principles of locomotive construction and operation displayed by young railway

" fans " has, indeed, been a remarkable feature of these trips.

The " King " locomotives drawing the excursion trains have shown their wonderful paces, and those who took the second excursion had the distinction of travelling behind

Photo] [South Wales News.

" Off to Swindon Works "—Cardiff schoolboys' visit.

" King Edward VII " from Swindon to London ($77\frac{1}{4}$ miles) at an average speed for the whole journey (start to stop) of nearly 68 miles an hour. The run was actually accomplished in exactly $68\frac{1}{2}$ minutes! Good going? Such is the pace of the " Kings."

CHAPTER THE EIGHTH

BRITAIN'S MIGHTIEST PASSENGER LOCOMOTIVE

THE "King" class of locomotives has several distinctive features, but the outstanding fact about these engines is their great hauling power, which is considerably higher than that of any other passenger locomotives in Great Britain. The hauling power of locomotives, as you already know, is technically referred to as "tractive effort," and that of the "Kings" at 85 per cent. of the boiler pressure is 40,300 lb.

It is on the basis of tractive effort at starting that the "King" locomotives claim their proud position as the most powerful passenger engines but, though the true limit of power is to be found in the boiler, it can be safely assumed that the designer has provided sufficient boiler power for the work which the engine has to perform.

"What do we mean exactly by tractive effort at 85 per cent. of boiler pressure?" Well, that is a fair question, and we will endeavour to answer it when we have had

" King George V." The prototype of the G.W.R. " King " Class of Passenger Locomotives.

a short descriptive chat about the mightiest of railway passenger engines.

It is particularly interesting to note how the greatly increased tractive effort of this class of locomotive has been obtained without exceeding the overall limits which were permitted in the earlier four-cylinder 4-6-0 type engines. The following table shows clearly the development of this type from its inception in 1906:

Date.	Class.	Tractive effort. lbs.	Weight of engine and tender. tons.	cwt.
1906	" North Star " (originally as 4-4-2)	25,085	114	10
1907	" Dog Star "	25,085	115	12
1913	" Prince of Wales "	27,800	115	12
1923	" Caerphilly Castle "	31,625	119	17
1927	" King George V "	40,300	135	14

Now take a look at this photographic diagram which gives the principal weights and dimensions of the " King " class engines and you will see that a total weight of 67 tons 10 cwt. is available for adhesion. This weight is distributed equally between the coupled wheels by means of compensating beams so that each axle carries a load of 22 tons 10 cwt. This loading is greater than that previously permitted, and for this reason special precautions had to be taken to ensure that the permanent way was sufficiently strong to carry the additional weight. The load on the bogie is 21 tons 10 cwt., which gives a total weight for the engine in working order (without tender) of 89 tons.

The tender is of the standard G.W.R. six-wheeled type, equipped with water pick-up apparatus, and weighs when

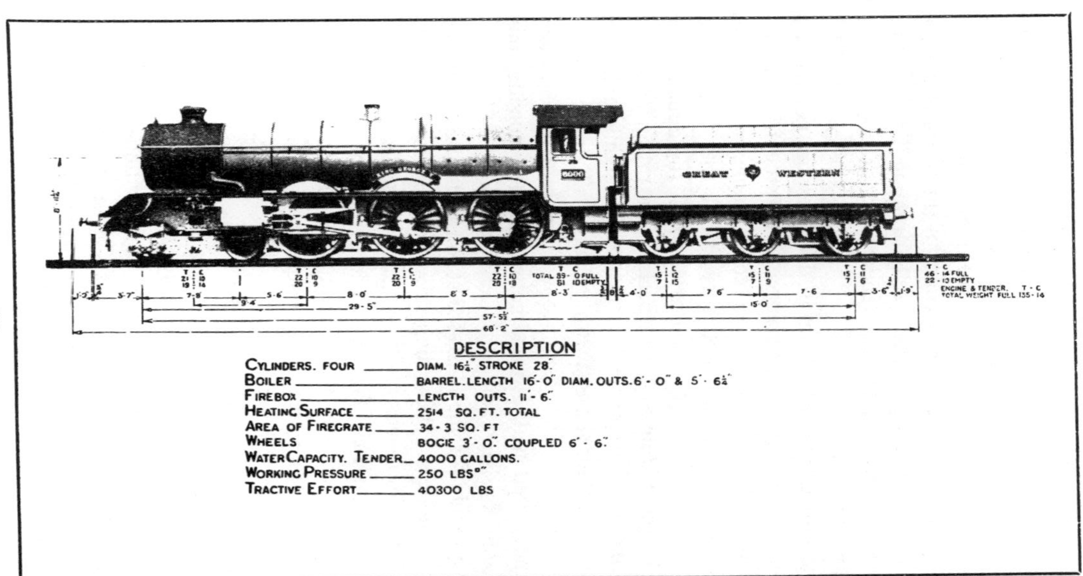

Principal Weights and Dimensions of " King " Locomotives.

full 46 tons 14 cwt., having a coal capacity of 6 tons and a water space for 4,000 gallons. As the coal is used from the tender it automatically feeds to the front owing to the slope of the coal space. It is on account of this feature that the tender is said to be of the "self-trimming" type. The weight of the engine and tender in working order is 135 tons 14 cwt.

The four cylinders, 16¼ in. in diameter, are not set in a line across the engine, but arranged so that the drive may be divided between the first and second coupled axles. The inside pair are placed well forward in the frames and drive on the leading coupled axle, whilst the outside pair drive on the middle coupled wheels. The piston stroke has been increased from 26 in. to 28 in. giving a higher tractive effort for starting with a heavy load, or for ascending gradients. The inside connecting rods have forked big ends fitted with gib and cotter, but the outside rods have solid bushed ends.

To provide for the increased steam consumption of the larger cylinders a new high-pressure superheater boiler (Standard No. 12) was designed with greater heating surface and firegrate area. The overall length of the firebox has been increased to 11 ft. 6 in. thus making it possible to obtain a firegrate area of 34·3 sq. ft. The total heating surface of the "King" class is 2,514 sq. ft. compared with 2,312 sq. ft. of the "Castle" class.

By providing ample boiler power in the "King" locomotives, not only is the available steam space sufficient to meet the varying requirements of the cylinders, but the large volume of water carried acts as a thermal storage which may be added to when the engine is working light, or may be drawn from when a heavy demand is made upon it.

As you have already been told the boiler pressure has been raised to the exceptional figure of 250 lb. per sq. in.,

The " King " funnel between those of 1837 and 1883.

thus enabling still further economies in the use of the steam to be effected.

The boiler is fitted with top feed, the water being fed through pipes in the safety-valve casting. Equalised vacuum braking is operated on all the coupled wheels. The cab is spacious, well protected by an extended roof and side windows, and fitted with audible signal gear for use over sections equipped for automatic train control.

As compared with the " Castle " class engines, we see that the overall length of the boiler has been increased from 24 ft. 10 in. to 27 ft. 6 in. For this reason it has been necessary to increase the coupled wheel base from 14 ft. 9 in. to 16 ft. 3 in. So that the engine may readily take curves with this extended wheel base, the trailing coupled wheels are allowed a considerable lateral movement, which is facilitated by the use of a ball-joint in the rod coupling the intermediate and trailing wheels. On a straight piece of track the weight of the engine acting on a series of inclined planes, automatically brings the trailing wheels back to their central position.

The diameter of the driving wheels has been reduced to 6 ft. 6 in. (as compared with the 6 ft. 8½ in. driving wheels of the "Castles"), resulting in a slight gain in tractive effort and enabling the engine to maintain a higher average speed up steep inclines without seriously affecting the maximum speeds of which she is capable on level stretches or on falling gradients.

New features are presented by the bogie, which is spring controlled, and of unique design. It has outside bearings on the leading axle and inside bearings on the trailing axle. This feature is necessitated by the desire to have independent springing for each of the bogie wheels, and for this reason the springs on the leading wheels are placed outside the bogie frame so as to clear the inside cylinders, which, you will remember, are placed well forward. The springs on the trailing wheels are placed on the inside of the bogie frame so as to clear the outside cylinders.

Although so much has been done to increase the power of the locomotive, I think you will agree that the appearance of the "Kings" has in no wise been neglected, and, as turned out from Swindon, with artistically lined-out panels and boiler bands, polished brass cab and splasher bead-

[*Railway Gazette.*

Underside of " King " Locomotive, showing Crank Axle, Inside Connecting Rods, Bogie Pin, etc.

ings, and copper-topped chimney, they are second to none in their delightful blending of grace and power.

Twenty engines of this class, named after the Kings of England, have already been built. As you know, No. 6000, the first to be completed, was appropriately named after our present monarch "King George V." The complete list is as follows :—

No.		No.	
6000	"King George V"	6010	"King Charles I"
6001	"King Edward VII"	6011	"King James I"
6002	"King William IV"	6012	"King Edward VI"
6003	"King George IV"	6013	"King Henry VIII"
6004	"King George III"	6014	"King Henry VII"
6005	"King George II"	6015	"King Richard III"
6006	"King George I"	6016	"King Edward V"
6007	"King William III"	6017	"King Edward IV"
6008	"King James II"	6018	"King Henry VI"
6009	"King Charles II"	6019	"King Henry V"

You will not be surprised to hear that the great ingenuity and ability displayed in designing and producing this new type of locomotive earned numerous congratulations for the Chief Mechanical Engineer and his skilled assistants and staff, all of whom entered whole-heartedly into the work, and I am sure you will agree that their product is deserving of the highest praise.

ꟹ ꟹ ꟹ ꟹ

And now let us see if we can understand just what is meant by that rather technical sort of term "tractive effort."

The force which a locomotive exerts in hauling a load is termed its tractive effort, and the maximum force thus exerted—that required at the moment of starting—is

C. W. R. LOCOMOTIVES

REPRODUCED TO THE SAME SCALE

"NORTH STAR" ——— As CONSTRUCTED BY R. STEPHENSON & Co IN 1837.
"LORD OF THE ISLES" ——— BUILT BY C. W. R. Co. AT SWINDON IN 1851.
"KINC CEORCE V" ——— DO. DO. DO. DO. DO. 1927.

ENGINE	CYLINDERS		DRIVINC WHEELS	BOILER PRESSURE	TRACTIVE EFFORT AT 85% BOILER PRESSURE
	Nº	DIMENSIONS			
NORTH STAR	2	16 × 16"	7 _ 0"	50 LBS.º"	2070 LBS.
"LORD OF THE ISLES"	2	18 × 24	8 _ 0"	140 "	9640 "
"KINC CEORCE V"	4	16¼ × 28	6 _ 6"	250 "	40300 "

commonly accepted as the basis for comparing the power of different engines.

Now, in determining this maximum value five factors have to be considered, namely, the number and the diameter of the cylinders, the length of piston stroke, the diameter of the driving wheels, and the pressure of steam acting on the pistons. You will readily appreciate that the greater the number and the diameter of the cylinders, and the longer the piston stroke, the greater will be the tractive effort, but the effect of the diameter of the driving wheels is, perhaps, hardly as obvious.

You know that with a bicycle or a motor-car, when there is hard work ahead, the machine or engine has to be put into "low gear" in order that greater pull or turning effort may be obtained. Well, that is equivalent to reducing the diameter of the wheels, as for the same number of revolutions of the crank or engine the cycle or car covers a smaller distance. Now, although in a railway locomotive there are no intermediate gears to effect such a change, the same principles hold good. Thus, if two locomotives are identical in every respect, save that they have driving wheels of different diameters, then the engine with the smaller wheels will have the greater tractive effort though for each revolution it will move a less distance.

This constitutes the essential difference between freight and passenger locomotives. The former are required to handle immense loads at comparatively low speeds and are provided with small diameter wheels; the latter deal with lighter loads, but as they are required to travel at much higher speeds, they have wheels of larger diameter.

There still remains the effect of the steam pressure.

It is obvious that the higher the pressure the greater will be the tractive effort, but before we can proceed further we must know the average force exerted on the piston throughout the stroke. You must know that steam will only flow towards a region of lower pressure, so there will be a

slight drop between the pressure of the steam in the boiler and of that in the steam chest ; and in no locomotive is the steam admitted to the cylinders throughout the *whole* of the stroke. With the engine in full gear the supply of steam is cut off at about 75 per cent. of the stroke and thereafter acts expansively on the piston. The result is that at starting the average pressure is about 85 per cent. of the boiler pressure. I hope that is clear.

The combined effect of these various factors is expressed in the formula :

$$\text{tractive effort} = \frac{n}{2} \times \frac{0{\cdot}85p \times d^2 \times l}{D} \text{ lb.}$$

where n = number of cylinders.
p = boiler pressure in lb. per sq. in.
d = diameter of cylinders in inches.
l = length of stroke in inches.
D = diameter of driving wheels in inches.

Now, by inserting the appropriate figures we find that the tractive effort of the " King " class of locomotives is 40,300 lb. at starting, nearly forty times as great as some of the earliest engines delivered to the G.W.R. Company, in spite of the fact that the latter were built to the broad gauge.

You may have noticed a letter painted on the side of the cab of G.W.R. locomotives and wondered what it meant. That letter denotes to the initiated within what limits the tractive effort of the locomotive falls.

It would be of little use designing a locomotive with a huge tractive effort unless provision was also made for sufficient weight to be carried on the driving wheels, as otherwise the wheels would slip instead of gripping the rails. When the rails are quite dry and free from grease, slipping will only occur if the tractive effort exceeds about one-third of the weight on the wheels but, if the rails are damp or greasy, a much smaller effort will suffice. Practical experience has shown that an adhesive weight of about $3\frac{3}{4}$ times the tractive effort is sufficient to secure reasonable freedom from slipping without unduly restricting the power of the engine.

Whilst on this subject you will probably want to know something about the horse-power which is developed by a locomotive. It is not possible to apply a fixed horse-power rating to locomotives as is done with motor-cars, as such factors as speed, load, gradients, wind resistance, and climatic conditions generally vary with, and indeed during, each journey. Under maximum conditions, however, a horse-power somewhat in excess of two thousand will be developed in the cylinders of locomotives of the " King " class ; and of that some sixteen hundred horse-power will be available at the tender draw-bar for hauling the train.

Yes, it is quite true that horse-powers of this order are developed by internal combustion engines—notably by aero-engines—of much less bulk, but it must be remembered that in the latter case the engine is revolving at extremely high speeds and that, therefore, the pulling power or tractive effort is correspondingly low. I can assure you that an aero-engine would be of little use in starting from rest a train of 500 tons, and that is the everyday duty of the " King " locomotives.

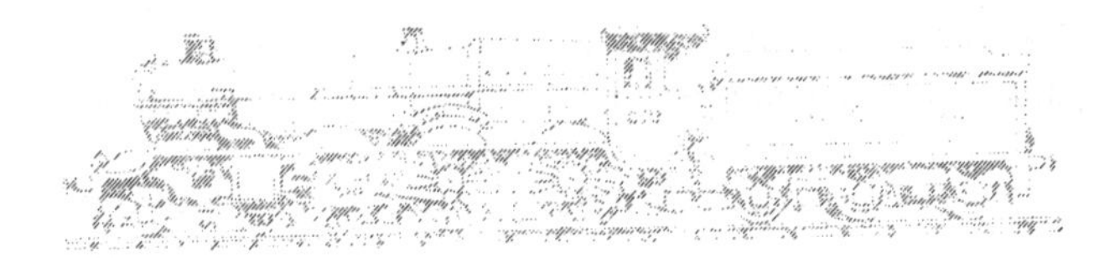

CHAPTER THE NINTH

"KING GEORGE V" IN AMERICA

THE railway locomotive made its appearance in America soon after its introduction in this country, and last year the Baltimore and Ohio Railroad, the first American railroad company to operate its line for the public handling of passengers and freight, held its centenary celebrations which, known as " The Fair of the Iron Horse," and described as " A World's Fair of Transportation," included a pageant of railway locomotives of all ages and many countries.

England, the mother of railways, was invited to contribute to this review, and " King George V," the latest type of Great Western Railway engine and the most powerful passenger locomotive in Great Britain, was sent overseas, accompanied by the rebuilt " North Star."

Shipment was carried out at Roath Dock, Cardiff, on August 3, into S.S. *Chicago City*. The two engines had been sent from Swindon to Cardiff the preceding day, by a special train which consisted of engine No. 6000 " King

George V," tender, and a crocodile wagon carrying the "North Star."

The new locomotive was shipped in three sections, *i.e.* boiler, tender, and undercarriage, by means of a 70-ton crane at the dock-side, and safely stowed without any untoward incident. One of these photographs shows the

" King George V " goes overseas : being unloaded at Cardiff Docks, November 26, 1927.

well-fitting " cradle " provided to ensure stability and " comfort " on the voyage.

The arrival of the " King George V " had been keenly looked forward to in America ; and not by railwaymen alone, as will be seen from these quotations from the *New York Herald Tribune*. The article was entitled " A Distinguished Envoy."

The Great Western Railway of England will send as an exhibit to the Baltimore and Ohio centenary this fall the

[Topical

Swinging the Boiler on board S.S. *Chicago City*.

[Topical

The Boiler on its cradle on S.S. *Chicago City*.

first of its new " King " class of locomotives. Breathes there a man with soul so dead that he doesn't thrill a little to such news ? Especially when he learns that this engine, now under construction, will be capable of a speed of eighty miles an hour, the most powerful locomotive ever built for an English railway.

Somewhere in the breast of every normal *homo sapiens* there stretches a chord that vibrates only to the sight of a fine locomotive. Even now, with airplanes and motors to bid against it in its own field of romantic interest, the steam locomotive retains its fascination. There are probably a number of reasons for this. We can think of at least two—its unusually demonstrative nature and its extraordinary beauty.

Man has devised no other machine that expresses its feelings so frankly and unmistakably. A locomotive sighs, it pants, it coughs, it barks ; it emits impassioned shrieks and mournful toots ; it puts forth powerful staccato protests at hauling a heavy load or climbing a steep grade ; it purrs ecstatically as it romps along the rails at a mile a minute ; it can hiss and throb and snort and tinkle. And in addition to all these auditory forms of expression it has its visual signs, its plumes of steam spelling surplus energy, its belchings of black smoke denoting determination, its sparks at night registering passion.

This new English locomotive that is coming over, the first of its race to pay us a visit since the Chicago World's Fair in 1893, will bear the name " King George V " and be one of twenty, each bearing the name of an English monarch.

The Great Western Railway locomotives " ancient and modern " arrived at Baltimore on August 21. Prior to being shipped " King George V " had been fitted with central drawgear and Westinghouse brake apparatus so as to permit of her operating on the American railroads.

Upon arrival the engines were conveyed from the quayside, Locust Point, Baltimore, to the Mount Clare shops of the Baltimore and Ohio Railroad in Baltimore, where the parts were reassembled in readiness for the Exhibition. The men working in the Mount Clare shops were im-

Unloading at Locust Point, Baltimore.

Unloading the undercarriage at Locust Point, Baltimore.

mensely interested in the details of construction and design of the engine, and frequently remarked, " It is not a locomotive, but an automobile."

The Exhibition, which was held from September 24 to October 15, was visited by over a million and a quarter people. " King George V " led the procession of big engines, and was accorded a great reception on every occasion. The general public, as well as railroad officers, remarked particularly the absence of smoke from the Great Western engine, both when standing and when running on the track.

You have doubtless made the acquaintance of American railways through the medium of the cinema, and will be aware from the films shown in this country that the tracks " out West " are not fenced from end to end, as they are in this country, from straying animals, human and otherwise. This will enable you to appreciate the surprise shown by visitors to the Exhibition at the absence on " King George V " of such essential features of equipment as powerful head-lights to illuminate the track, and a clanging bell, to warn those who use the railway track as a highway, and approaching road vehicles when in the vicinity of level crossings. Likewise your knowledge of the expressive slang employed for American film captions will enable you to understand how on these unfenced tracks " hobos jump the rattlers " or, as we should say in our more prosaic language, how tramps steal rides on the freight trains, in that country of wide spaces and wondrous phrases.

It was apparently as difficult for the average American citizen to understand that the railway in England is fenced in, and therefore not available for the general public to

A contrast: An American Locomotive and—

"King George V" at the Exhibition.

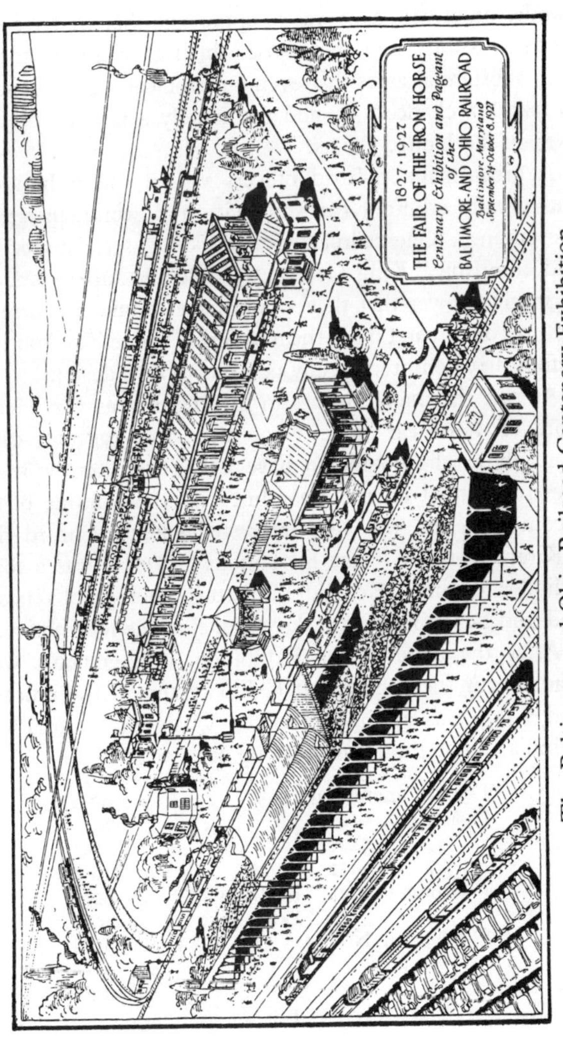

The Baltimore and Ohio Railroad Centenary Exhibition.

wander on at will, as it was to appreciate that we have few grade crossings, and that those which exist are protected with substantial gates that even a motor-car would hesitate to take "a chance" at, and not merely a pivoted pole as used in the United States.

A great many railroad officers visited the Exhibition, and greatly admired the simplicity and workmanship of the engine. One railroad vice-president, after inspecting and admiring "King George V," told his superintendent of motive power that they would have to take a course of lectures on art, and study the meaning of "line" and outline before they ventured on any new locomotive designs.

Among the many visitors to the engine was Mr. Henry Ford of Ford car fame, who, after the pageant, came specially to the engine to have a short trip on the track. He commented on the smoothness of the working of the locomotive, and was very interested when he heard that "King George V" like his famous "Ford" was a four-cylinder engine. He had numerous photographs taken, and said he intended to make a model of the locomotive.

After the close of the Exhibition, arrangements were made to run the engine, attached to a train, on the railroad, and a trip was arranged between Washington and Philadelphia. The train was made up of:

	Tons.
Dynamometer car	65·0
Coach No. 5411	76·2
" 5427	76·2
" 5422	76·2
Pullman sleeper "East Falls"	80·0
" " "Loch Awe"	80·0
Official car No. 97	90·0
	543·6

"KING GEORGE V" IN AMERICA

" King George V " on her trial trip in America.

The train ran from Camden station to Washington, and from Washington to Philadelphia. On account of the water troughs standing below the rail level it was not possible for " King George V " to use them, so stops for water had to be made at two points, Camden station and Elk Mills.

The fuel used was a hard gas coal, and hardly suitable for the long run of 271·8 miles with the type of grate on the " King " locomotives, and some difficulty was experienced in maintaining steam at full pressure on account of the amount of clinker formed. The Great Western Railway engineman and fireman did not, of course, know the road they were travelling or the coal they were using, but the railroad officials on the train were very satisfied with the result, and were particularly pleased with the riding of the engine, the way it took the curves, and its smooth working. The Baltimore and Ohio Company did not desire speeds in excess of 65 m.p.h. on this section of road, on account of curves and the numerous grade crossings. Representatives of the Pennsylvania and the Delaware and Hudson Railroads were on the train, in addition to many of the Baltimore and Ohio officers.

The " North Star " (1837) attracted a good deal of attention at the Exhibition, particularly as on the same road and near the " North Star " were the Braithwaite "Rocket," built in 1838 by Braithwaite and Co., of London, for the Reading Railroad, America, " Samsen," Canada's first locomotive, built in England by Timothy Hackworth in 1838, and " The Albion," Canada's second engine, built by Timothy Hackworth in 1839. The contrast between " North Star " and these engines, constructed a year or two later, was most striking for " North Star " was

“ King George V ” leading the procession of Locomotives at the Baltimore and Ohio Railroad Centenary Exhibition.

modern in appearance, whereas the other engines had hardly advanced beyond the old " Rocket " period.

The " Fair of the Iron Horse " was an unqualified success, and undoubtedly the presence of the Great Western Railway engines, where " King George V " was the sole representative of modern British locomotives, did much to increase the interest in the Exhibition, and to enhance the prestige of British railways.

It was a pure coincidence, but rather an extraordinary one, that while the Great Western Railway of England had been producing its first engine of the " King " class, designated " King George V," the Baltimore and Ohio Railroad had introduced a new " President " class of which the prototype was " President Washington."

The interest which " King George V " excited and the part she played in the success of the Exhibition can, perhaps, best be judged by an extract from a letter sent by the President of the Baltimore and Ohio Railroad to the General Manager of the Great Western Railway :

> I doubt if I can tell you how greatly the " King George " and the " North Star "—but more particularly the " King George "—contributed to the success of our exposition. While some people in the United States have visited England, and are acquainted with the appearance of English railway equipment, of course a very large majority of our people have never been abroad, and to them an English locomotive, and particularly as beautiful a machine as the " King George," was something of more than ordinary interest. You would have been glad, I am sure, if you could have heard the applause which greeted the appearance of the " King George " as she moved by the reviewing stand each day in the pageant.

Many English visitors to the " Fair of the Iron Horse " at Baltimore wrote to say how proud they were to see such

" King George V " at the Baltimore and Ohio Railroad Centenary Exhibition, 1927.

a fine example of British locomotive engineering as " King George V." The sentiments they expressed are crystallised by the correspondent who, referring to the Great Western Railway engine, said, " It has done England much good."

Some of the American newspaper reports of the run by " King George V " with a train over the Baltimore and Ohio track were informative in their own delightfully descriptive manner, with just that touch of American journalese in which the U.S.A. pressman excels. Here is a brief extract from an article in the *Baltimore Sun* of October 18, 1927, under the headline " Touches 76-Mile-an-Hour Rate " :

> . . . at one point on its return from the capital to this city, it touched a speed of 76 miles an hour on a favourable length of track. Then, even through the haze of cigar smoke, a tenseness in the atmosphere of the dynamometer car was evident. The spirit of the " King George V " seemed to be expanding and taking wings. But its flight was short lived.
>
> " Cut that out ! Pipe down ! " a voice from somewhere in the car said.
>
> An official picked up the telephone that communicates with the cab, and the needle on the dial began sinking to sixty, then to forty-five, then lower still. The time taken by the " King George V " in making the Washington-to-Baltimore run was announced as forty-four minutes.

Under the startling title " Great Britain's Revolution " these paragraphs appeared in the *Ottawa Citizen* two days later :

> Many people abroad have been led to believe that Great Britain hovers on the brink of revolution. There are signs that the revolution is developing, but it is quite different from the picture which pessimistic people have needlessly feared.
>
> One recent manifestation of the British revolution appeared

last Monday on the Baltimore and Ohio railway tracks. A British locomotive, bearing the name "King George V", astonished officials of the American railroad by running at 76 miles an hour with its throttle only 75 per cent. open.

Labourers, office workers, and motorists along the route from Baltimore to Washington and thence to Philadelphia and back to Baltimore craned their necks as the locomotive swept by with seven coaches. With no pipes and few working parts exposed, the streamlined British engine appeared very different from the usual American type.

It must have surprised many, too, to see the brightly painted green engine, with shining steel parts and polished brass work. In addition to giving the speed and having the appearance, it is safe to say that the British locomotive has the qualities of endurance that inhere in British workmanship.

Baltimore and Ohio Railroad Centenary Medal, awarded to "King George V."

"King George V" was awarded the medals struck in commemoration of the Baltimore and Ohio Railroad centenary and was also presented with a large brass bell similar to those carried on American locomotives. The engine now carries the medals on the side of her cab and the bell on her buffer plate. The latter is inscribed :

Presented to Locomotive King George V
by the
Baltimore and Ohio Railroad Company
in commemoration of its
Centenary Celebration
Sept. 24th–Oct. 15th, 1927.

There has recently been an interesting sequel to the visit of " King George V " to America, for the Baltimore and Ohio Railroad Company has constructed in its Mount Clare workshops a new locomotive which embodies many features of the G.W.R. engine.

As you can see by the photograph, the new engine, named " President Cleveland," bears resemblance to " King George V," whilst most of the " gadgets " which are such familiar exterior features of American locomotives have been concealed in accordance with British practice.

You will not need to be told that the Great Western

" King George V " with Bell presented by the Baltimore and Ohio Railroad Company.

Railway fully appreciates the high compliment paid it by the Baltimore and Ohio Railroad in producing a "Presi-

The "*King*" locomotive of the Baltimore and Ohio Railroad.

dent" so closely resembling a "King."

∽ ∽ ∽ ∽

And now, I really think, you ought to know a little more than most boys about "The 'King' of Railway Locomotives"—in theory at any rate. An ounce of practice is worth a ton of theory, however, and knowing something of your interest in the subject, the General Manager of the Great Western Railway has kindly consented to your taking a trip on the footplate of one of the "Kings." So, if you will be at Paddington Station at 10.20 a.m. to-morrow you will have the opportunity—unique I believe for a boy of your age—of making the "non-stop" run from Paddington to Plymouth in the cab of a "King" locomotive, hauling our old friend "The 10.30 Limited," and of seeing something of the engine's powers and paces.

Till to-morrow then. . . .

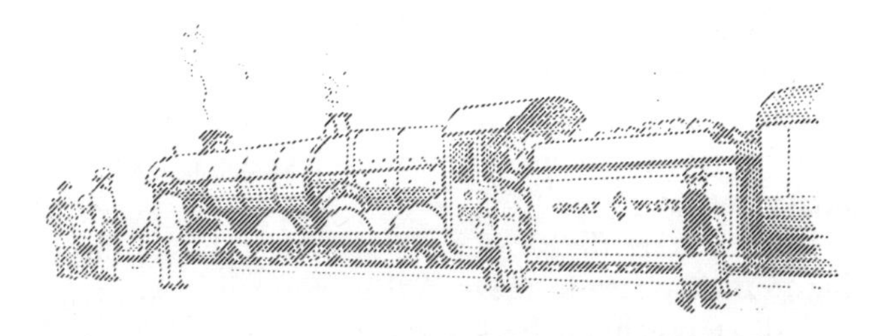

CHAPTER THE TENTH

A FOOTPLATE TRIP ON "KING GEORGE V"

YOU are early, but just in time to see the carriages of "The 10.30 Limited" being brought into No. 1 Platform by one of the "4500" class (2–6–2) tank engines which are largely employed on these duties. Since their last trip all the coaches forming our train have been thoroughly cleaned at Old Oak Common carriage sheds and have come to Paddington over the carriage road which now crosses the main line by an overbridge, thus obviating the possibility of delay whilst waiting for the main line to clear.

As is usual at this season of the year we find the platform thronged with happy holiday makers, who are travelling by this famous train, and, as you see by the label boards on the carriages, there are through coaches to quite a large number of holiday resorts.

The smartly uniformed guards, each in charge of his own section of this train of many destinations, are assisting their passengers, whilst porters are stowing away luggage in the various vans. Apparently many of these travellers are still unaware of the advantages of sending their baggage ahead under a reliable "luggage in advance" arrangement.

There you see the Registered Seats Porters busily directing to their places in the train those passengers who have had the foresight to book seats in advance. The registration of seats is a growing practice on the Great Western Railway, and as many as 15,000 seats have been booked on trains leaving this station during a single Saturday in the height of the holiday season.

You notice that there is an atmosphere of joyful anticipation amongst our passengers. That is quite the right holiday spirit. They are doubtless looking forward to the blue seas, golden sands, and glorious sunshine of the West Country with (I dare say) a thought of "splits and cream" for tea. I think you will agree that it is an attractive prospect, particularly as all those enjoyments are to be prefaced by a speedy railway journey through some of the best stretches of our delightful English countryside.

You see these travellers are *not* worried by pot-holes, the perfume of petrol, or the dangerous proximity of racing motor-coaches. Nervous tension and the risks of congested highways are alike absent and they can read in comfort, enjoy a meal, and (if they feel so inclined) a quiet nap while speeding to their respective holiday destinations. Railway travel in these days of powerful locomotives, perfect tracks, well-appointed corridor coaches, modern restaurant cars and allotted seats is surely travel at its very best. These fortunate folks are actually

"The 10.30 Limited" at No. 1 Platform, Paddington Station.

beginning their holidays here at Paddington Station, for such travel as theirs is a joy in itself.

There are fourteen coaches on the train to-day, six for the Cornish Riviera proper, including a restaurant car which goes right through to Penzance; a seventh which will come off at Plymouth (and proceed to Newquay); two coaches to be slipped at Exeter, one of which will go on to Kingsbridge; three more to be slipped at Taunton (for Minehead and Ilfracombe), and finally, the last two coaches, which form the first slip portion, and come off at Westbury, to go on to Weymouth.

If we take a look at the white figures painted on the ends of the coaches we can get an idea of the weight of our train for the several stages of its journey. Thus we find that the load to-day from Paddington to Westbury is 485 tons, from Westbury to Taunton 412 tons, from Taunton to Exeter 325 tons, and from Exeter to Plymouth 255 tons. These are the weights of the coaches behind the tender without their loads of passengers and luggage, but if we want to arrive at the actual weight hauled we can do so fairly accurately by reckoning sixteen passengers and their luggage to the ton. In a calculation of this kind we can even afford to ignore a small boy on the footplate.

We will put our watches right by the big clock overhead and proceed to the front of the train where our engine is already silently backing on to the train. As usual, we see a small and enthusiastic band of locomotive lovers "of all ages," feasting their eyes and filling their notebooks with particulars of "King George V," proudly carrying on the buffer-plate the bell brought back from the Baltimore and Ohio Railroad Centenary Exhibition in

America laſt year. We are certainly lucky in having the first of the " Kings " on this run to-day.

As the locomotive comes to reſt the fireman slips down from the footplate and couples the engine shackle and carriage drawbar hook, screwing them up tightly. He also connects the engine vacuum pipe.

Now let us ſtep up and introduce ourselves to the driver and fireman in whose company we are to make our trip to Plymouth. . . .

We muſt make ourselves as small as possible and keep out of the way. Thanks to the roominess of the cab of the " King " class that is easier than on some engines. Another feature about the cab of the " King " class, which is at once noticeable, is the excellent lighting afforded by the large front and side windows, or " lights " as they are called.

Now the driver teſts the vacuum brake by opening the ejector ſteam valve and " blowing-up " until, as you see, 25 in. of vacuum registered by the train pipeneedle on the engine gauge. He then closes the ejector ſteam valve and notes the rate at which the needle falls back towards the zero position. Watch how slowly it drops. That indicates that there is no serious leakage of air into the train pipe. If the rate of fall had been excessive the driver would have reported the fact to a train examiner, who would locate and remedy the defect.

In the meantime the guard will also have tested the brake by lifting the brake setter in the last van of the train, thus admitting air into the train pipe and so partially destroying the vacuum. He has ensured that the brake is working continuously throughout the whole length of the train by the gauge needle in the van again recording the requisite vacuum as our driver " blows-up."

A few minutes remain before we are due to start and you see the driver employs them by going round his engine, giving it a final look-over and an oiling here and there. Meanwhile the fireman judiciously regulates the supply of water from the tender to the boiler so that the steam pressure is kept just below the " blowing-off " point of 250 lb. per sq. in.

The guard has been along and reported to the driver the load of the train in tons and the number of wheels behind the tender. Look out on the left and you will see that our starting signal is " off." . . . There goes the guard's whistle and if you consult your watch, for with such a long train we are rather too far away to see the station clock, you will see that it is precisely ten-thirty. Our driver opens the regulator for we feel the engine move forward ever so gently. We have started on our four hours' " non-stop " run of 226 miles to Plymouth Bon voyage.

∽ ∽ ∽ ∽

Keep your eye on our driver and you will see him move the regulator first to about a quarter of the way open, and then to the half or three-quarter position. This gradual opening is made in order to avoid the wheels slipping on the rails. Had these been at all wet or greasy the driver would have sanded them in order to give the wheels a better grip.

Those handles so conveniently placed for the driver's use operate the sanding gear. The drain cocks, which

The Cab of the " King " Locomotive.

have been left open for a little while on starting, in order to blow out any water which may have condensed in the cylinders whilst the engine has been standing at the station, are now closed. The ejector steam valve, which was open just before starting so as to create and maintain a vacuum of 25 in. and to enable us to move off immediately the " right away " was given, is also now closed and the vacuum is maintained by an air pump operated from one of the engine crossheads.

As you probably know, the force required to start or to accelerate a train is very much greater than that necessary to keep it moving at a uniform rate. Now, as our speed increases, full advantage is taken of the properties of high-pressure steam by limiting the supply to the cylinders at each stroke and allowing it to act expansively on the piston. This results in more economical working of the engine. You noticed that at starting the engine was placed in full fore gear. In this position, as you already know, steam is admitted to the cylinders for about 75 per cent. of the piston stroke, but as the speed of the train increases and the force required decreases, the engine is " notched-up," as the drivers say, by putting the reversing gear towards its mid-position and so cutting off the supply of steam to the cylinders at an earlier point in the stroke. The minimum period of admission (or point of cut-off) in which the engine normally works is about 15 per cent., and should there be need for still further reduction of the force acting on the pistons, then this is effected by slightly closing the regulator.

We cannot very well watch both the driver and the fireman at once, but it is high time we paid a little attention to our stoker friend. Before starting he has seen that the boiler is filled with water to the level of the top of the gauge glass and that both injectors were then shut off. As the train moves off he stirs the fire with a pricker in order to assist the strong blast, produced by the exhaust steam, in pulling the fire round into its working condition. The needle of the pressure-gauge, which you see has dropped some 5 or 10 lb., owing to the heavy demand made on the boiler at starting, now gradually rises to the blowing-off point again.

The fireman now commences feeding the furnace. Watch him carefully as he goes about it. Throwing in three or four shovelsful of coal at a time, he gradually works round the firebox, so that while the coal is right up to the level of the firehole door at the back it is fairly thin at the front. Notice how careful he is to keep the firehole flap-plate in position between the periods of firing and, indeed, in between each shovelful of coal. This precaution is necessary in order that as little cold air as possible may reach the firebox. Despite his care, however, the boiler pressure does drop slightly with each period of firing, partly owing to the admission of cold air and partly due to the heat of the fire being checked by the fresh coal thrown upon it.

Looking at the gauge glass we see that the level of the water has gradually dropped, for up to the present our engine has been working on the water which was in the boiler at the time of starting the journey. As the " clock " or pressure-gauge again comes round to the 250 lb. per sq. in. indication, you see that the left-hand or exhaust injector is started to work. This injector is somewhat different from that we saw on the " Castle " class engine, for it automatically changes over from exhaust working to an ordinary restarting live steam injector when the regulator is shut and a supply of exhaust steam is no longer available. The adoption of this new type of injector considerably reduces the work of the fireman, as it is no longer necessary for him to shut off the left-hand injector and put on the right-hand (live steam) injector every time that the regulator is closed.

While we have been chatting we have got under way and are now passing Westbourne Park Station at a speed of 30 miles an hour. The cut-off has been reduced from the 75 per cent. at starting to 30 per cent. and our speed is now rapidly increasing. We pass the extensive engine and carriage sheds at Old Oak Common and are soon through Acton and the Ealings. Now Hanwell is behind us, and as we reach Southall we have overhauled the 60 miles an hour mark and the gear is being "notched-up" to 17 per cent. Passing Hayes and Harlington we get on to a short stretch of slightly falling gradient, and with the gear at 16 per cent., we are through Slough Station and doing nearly 70 miles an hour. We have covered the 18½ miles from Paddington in exactly 20 minutes. Not too bad.

As you have seen, the water feed to the boiler has been adjusted from time to time, and it is now so regulated that the boiler demand is just met and the height of water in the gauge glass kept constantly at working level.

Our busy fireman keeps placing four or five shovelsful of coal on the fire every minute. He believes in the golden rule of "little and often." He has also adjusted his ashpan dampers so that the boiler is steaming freely with the gauge needle hovering around the 250 lb. per sq. in. mark.

Every now and then the fireman waters the coal and the footplate in order to keep the dust down. He takes the water from either of these injector delivery pipes through this coal watering cock which you see is placed in a handy position on the side of the cab.

Meanwhile our driver has adjusted his hydrostatic sight-feed lubricator so that each minute about fifteen to twenty drops of oil are delivered to the cylinders and, beyond an occasional glance at the gauges to see that everything is O.K., his chief concern now is to keep a good look-out ahead. Take a look through the spectacle and see how the lines appear to be rushing towards us as we speed onwards.

I thought you would be asking sooner or later what the ringing of that bell means. If you notice, we get a ring every time we pass a " distant " signal. The bell is part of the audible signalling installation on this section of line—from London to Reading. You will remember we had a talk about audible signalling on your previous trip by this train (when you were a mere passenger).* There is a shoe on our engine which makes electrical contact with a ramp fixed between the rails at distant signals and the contact rings the bell in our cab when the signal is " off." If the signal was " on "—at " danger "—it would not only sound a siren to warn the driver, but also automatically apply the brakes to ensure the train being stopped before reaching the home signal. You can appreciate what a help and relief this is to engine-drivers, particularly in foggy weather, or when for any reason the signals cannot be clearly seen.

Another little duty which the engine crew have to attend to in winter is the maintenance of a comfortable degree of steam heating on the train. This is checked by reference

* See "The 10.30 Limited."

to the steam heating gauge, which is kept at round about 80 lb. per sq. in. under winter conditions.

We are speeding through the Thames Valley at a comfortable 68 miles an hour on a slightly rising gradient of 1 in 1320. Now we cross the Thames by Maidenhead Bridge and get the longest run so far without a station—between Maidenhead and Twyford. Passing Twyford Station, we are soon in Sonning cutting and on the right get another view of the Thames, whilst on our left we see Reading's famous biscuit factory. Look at your watch and you will see that we have reached Reading (36 miles from London) at 11.6 a.m., so we have taken exactly 36 minutes to cover the 36 miles. Here we get our first check and, as you see, the driver closes the regulator leaving it in the "coasting" or "drifting" position to make sure that the cylinders are still getting lubrication. He drops the gear back to the position of 45 per cent. cut-off, which position, I may tell you, experience has shown, results in a minimum of smokebox gases being drawn down the blast-pipe and least wear on the valves when the engine is drifting. Take a look back and see how gracefully our long train takes these curves.

The fireman so arranges his duties that he can assist his driver in keeping a sharp look-out for signals when passing through busy junctions or stations, and you will see they are both particularly alert at such times.

We get a slight application of the brakes here, and with a reduction of speed we are through Reading Station at 40 miles an hour, the maximum rate allowed on the curves here and at Southcote Junction just beyond.

We now have a long climb to Savernake, and rapidly

accelerating we are doing a mile a minute again by the time we reach Aldermaston. The fireman crosses to the driver's side of the cab and by means of the water pick-up handle lowers the scoop under the tender, for here are the Aldermaston water-troughs—the first place at which we take water on this trip.

Look out ahead. There are the water-troughs glistening in the sun. They seem to be racing towards us. . . . Now we are over them and below the tender the scoop is cutting off the water, which rushes upwards into the tank where it is trapped. Watch the indicator and see how rapidly the tank fills. There you are—2,000 gallons picked up in fifteen seconds! Our engine has had a long drink but a quick one. The scoop is already being raised by the fireman and in a flash the water-troughs (already refilling themselves) are away behind us, and we speed onwards without even a check.

You will get a better appreciation of the gradients encountered on our trip, and through to Penzance, if you take a look at this diagram of the road. It includes some stiffish climbs and it is no small tribute to the powers of the " Kings " that they have enabled the time for the run from London to Plymouth to be reduced by 7 minutes, to 4 hours exactly. This is accomplished, mark you, by a much higher average speed, but with an actual *reduction* in the maximum speed.

A steady speed of over 60 miles per hour is maintained over rising gradients varying from 1 in 300 to 1 in 600, with short intervening stretches of even steeper gradient, until the summit is nearly reached when a speed restriction of 50 miles per hour is enforced at Grafton Junction,

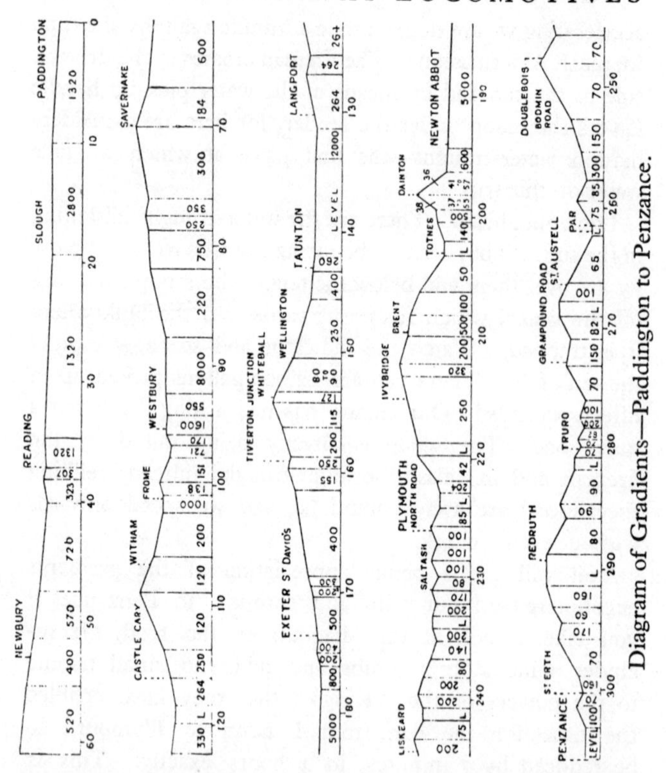

Diagram of Gradients—Paddington to Penzance.

notwithstanding which, and a final gradient of 1 in 145, Savernake is passed at 11.41 a.m., the 70 miles having been covered in 71 minutes. Notice as we pass over the top of the bank how the driver eases the regulator and brings the gear back from the 18 per cent., used in the last part of our climb, to 15 per cent.

Now we are going to do some speeding. See how we

are accelerating—65—68—71—75. Now we are through Patney and Chirton Station—still we get faster till we reach 78 and touch the " 80 m.p.h. " mark at Edington and Bratton. Here, however, speed has to be rapidly reduced and we fall back quickly to 60—45—and then to 30 miles an hour in order safely to negotiate sharp curves at Westbury and Frome.

This is Westbury and here we drop our first slip portion —the two coaches for Weymouth—and having done so we are soon again taking water, this time from the Westbury troughs. Witham Bank and Bruton are taken in our stride as we speed onwards through delightful " Sunny Somerset." At Somerton we enter the first tunnel on our journey, but such is our speed that you will be surprised to hear that it is 1,056 yards in length. . . . We are through it.

On we go, passing Athelney Marshes and sparing a thought for poor old King Alfred who hereabouts got a cuff from the swineherd's wife for spoiling her cakes—or so they told us at school. We soon join the old main line to the West of England at Cogload Junction; our engine takes another drink at the Creech troughs and, dropping our second slip portion, we pass Taunton at 12.51½ p.m., having covered the 143 miles from London in 141½ minutes.

Our load being now considerably lightened we face the ascent to Whiteball Tunnel, the famous Wellington Bank (which takes its name from the monument to the " Iron Duke," a landmark for many miles around) being taken at a minimum speed of 46 miles an hour with a maximum cut-off position of 25 per cent. It was over this piece of track, but in the reverse direction, that the fastest authoritative speed (102·3 m.p.h.) ever recorded on any railway was achieved. We here enter the longest tunnel on our journey (1,088 yards) and now having topped the bank a fast run downhill brings us to Exeter, where our third and last slip coaches are released at 1.21½ p.m. exactly.

A restriction in speed of 25 miles an hour is imposed through Exeter, but at Exminster we improve our running and take water from the Exminster troughs—the last drink for our engine on her run to Plymouth. Only moderate speed is now possible along the winding coastal route to Teignmouth, and this gives us an opportunity to enjoy the delightful Devonshire seascapes on our left. Look at the merry youngsters waving to us from the beach at Dawlish. Let's wave back. . . . I expect some of those boys rather envy you up here on the footplate.

Our sea views are here eclipsed from time to time by a series of five short tunnels through the rock between Dawlish and Teignmouth. The longest and last of these is Parson's tunnel, which is preceded by Clerk's tunnel. They are named after the " Parson and Clerk " rocks which stand out at sea on our left as we run alongside the sea-wall towards Teignmouth.

Now we leave the sea and turn inland and are soon approaching Newton Abbot. Look out on your left as we run through the station and you will get a glimpse—only a fleeting one, I fear—of the last old broad gauge locomotive in the world—excepting, of course the rebuilt " North

Star." This is the old engine " Tiny," now an exhibit on the Down Platform at Newton Abbot Station. She was built by Messrs. Sara and Company of Plymouth for the old South Devon Railway in 1869, and until fairly recently was employed as a stationary engine for working pumps at Newton Abbot.

" Tiny " was taken over by the Great Western Railway in 1876 and used for some time for shunting. Her G.W.R. number was 2180. You ought to have a look at this interesting relic when you are next in the locality. She has four coupled wheels of 3 ft. diameter and a vertical tubeless boiler. There she is . . .

" Tiny."

We are through the station and soon ready to take the Dainton Bank which rises sharply for nearly 2½ miles with such gradients as 1 in 57—46—41—and 44, respectively ; gradients which are equalled nowhere else in the world for main line express services similar to those of the Great Western Railway. Despite this, however, our powerful " King George V " takes them easily at 35 miles an hour. At the top of the climb we have Dainton tunnel—272 yards in length.

We get a steep descent into Totnes, but a succession of reverse curves limits our speed and we can't " let her out." There is some collar work ahead of us, for we are approaching Rattery Bank, the first part of which extends for 4½ miles and includes gradients of 1 in 47 and 1 in 54.

So you have noticed how the water gauge varies as we pass over the tops of these banks—or pass from a falling gradient to a rising one. That is due to changes in the inclination of the boiler, and the fireman has to allow for it and see that when climbing a bank he has sufficient water to ensure that the firebox will be covered when descending on the other side.

This is Marley tunnel—869 yards—and we are now getting towards the last stages of our journey. We pass Wrangaton, at the top of the bank and some 15 miles from Plymouth (North Road Station), and from now onwards you notice that the fireman puts very little coal on his fire. He is working it down so that there shall be a minimum of coal in the firebox when Plymouth is reached. That thick fire at the back of the box is gradually pushed forward as the thin part burns through, until at Plymouth there should be a thin fire spread evenly over the grate. With no fresh coal being added the fire burns with an intense heat and opportunity is taken to bring up the level of the water in the glass. As you can imagine, some amount of skill is required to work the fire down so that, while sufficient steam is maintained up to the end of the trip, unnecessary consumption of coal is avoided.

We are approaching Plymouth and, as you see, the driver tests the brakes by making a partial application. Satisfied as to their operation, he recreates a vacuum of 25 in., thus releasing the brakes again. After a rush up this short bank of 1 in 82, we are through our last tunnel (Mutley

—183 yards). Our speed now drops gradually and a gentle application of the brakes brings us to rest at North Road Station, the 226 miles from Paddington having been covered in exactly 4 hours at an average speed of nearly 56½ miles per hour.

Perhaps you noticed that immediately before stopping the brakes were released. This was done in order that the train could be brought to rest smoothly and without even a suspicion of a jerk.

In the course of our trip approximately 4 tons of coal have been burnt and about 8,000 gallons of water evaporated.

The log of the train will probably interest you and here it is, with the point-to-point speeds which I have jotted down:

		m.p.h.
Paddington .	10.30	
		55·4
Slough . . .	10.50	
		65·7
Reading . .	11.6	
		58.5
Savernake . .	11.41	
		66·4
Westbury . .	12·4	
		59·8
Taunton . .	12·51½	
		61·5
Exeter . . .	1.31½	
		50.9
Newton Abbot .	1.45½	
		43·0
North Road .	2.30	

Now we bid adieu to our friends the driver and fireman, who take their engine to shed, while one of the 2–6–0 type is attached to the train for the continuation of its journey to Penzance.

Quite a number of passengers are now alighting, for Plymouth, " The Centre of 100 Tours," is a well-favoured holiday resort. Visitors to the Cornish Riviera, who have arrived here from various parts of the country, soon take their places, however, and the train again has its complement of passengers.

Our train, originally of fourteen coaches, is now reduced to six only, for we have slipped seven *en route*, and, as you see, an eighth is now being detached and will take its passengers through to Newquay. Another coach will be put off at Truro for Falmouth, and yet another at St. Erth for St. Ives, so that only four of the fourteen coaches will arrive at Penzance, where they are due at 4.55 p.m.

I expect you will feel a bit stiff after your four hours' trip on a locomotive and miss the motion of the footplate, but that will soon wear off.

∽ ∽ ∽ ∽

We have certainly had a glorious run and you have been able to see at first hand what a wonderful machine the " King " locomotive is. We have actually *averaged* 56½ miles an hour " start to stop " on the mightiest passenger locomotive, over one of the finest stretches of railway (but one with some stiff gradients) for a 226 miles " non-stop " journey: a trip, by the way, which, I must remind you, is considerably faster than *any* other regular " non-stop " run of 200 miles or over.

But what I want particularly to emphasise is that, although the " King " locomotives have enabled the scheduled time of the famous run of " The 10.30 Limited " to be substantially reduced—with a heavier load, mark you

—the reduction has not been accomplished by any special burst of speed over a favourable stretch of track. No, the secret of the reduction in the time schedule lies entirely in the greater power of the " King " engines which maintain a higher *average* speed with an actual *reduction* in the maximum speed; which is, of course, the thing to be aimed at in good locomotive practice.

Though it is indeed a creditable achievement, this fine run is an everyday occurrence on a railway which, since the earliest days of railways, has been the pioneer of fast trains; just one example of G.W.R. SERVICE, shall we say? Little wonder that the first Minister of the Crown (who, by the way, is little given to superlatives or rhapsodies) said, in the House of Commons as recently as February 13 of this year, " the Great Western Railway has the finest system in the world."

You and I have never had any doubts on that point, have we? And now having stated a great truth and reached the end of a most enjoyable and instructive run, it can, I think, be said that we have both " arrived "; and this affords a suitable opportunity to say

AU REVOIR.